"Surely a dress like this is not suitable!"

Cindy felt shocked and disgusted at the flimsy red dress. How could Jason want to paint her wearing such a thing?

"Very suitable, indeed," he said softly. She heard him laugh. Then he reached out a hand and put it gently against her thigh. Slowly, tantalizingly, the hand moved, the long fingers brushing over the outward curve of her thigh to her hip, and up to her waist. She wanted to push his hand away, but she could not move. By now it was an effort just to breathe. His touch was torture to her frenzied senses.

"You are wrong," Jason said huskily.

"Wrong?" The word came out in a rasping whisper.

"The dress is more than suitable. Come along, Cindy...."

ROSEMARY CARTER
is also the author of these

Harlequin Presents

and these

Harlequin Romances

Many of these titles are available at your local bookseller.

For a free catalogue listing all available Harlequin Romances and Harlequin Presents, send your name and address to:

ROSEMARY CARTER

face in the portrait

Harlequin Books

TORONTO • LONDON • LOS ANGELES • AMSTERDAM
SYDNEY • HAMBURG • PARIS • STOCKHOLM • ATHENS • TOKYO

Harlequin Presents edition published February 1981
ISBN 0-373-10410-3

Original hardcover edition published in 1980
by Mills & Boon Limited

CHAPTER ONE

THE SOUTH COAST bus took the broad highway faster than usual, as if in a hurry to reach the terminal before the threatening storm could unleash the worst of its tropical fury. A few miles out of the village of Sea View it stopped briefly, to allow two people to alight—a young girl with a small boy.

Normally more than a few of the passengers would have shown interest in the slender figure with hips that swayed gracefully beneath a softly flaring skirt. Her auburn hair feathered naturally away from a well-cut oval face, and her eyes, beneath delicately winged eyebrows, were wide and clear and as green as the turbulent sea.

Today, however, all thoughts were on the approaching storm. As the bus sped farther on not a single head was turned.

It was very hot, with a heat that gripped the

tropical coastlands of Natal summer and winter. The sky was swollen with black cloud, and the wind bent the banana palms double and churned the ocean into boiling mountains of foam. It was no weather for a child to be out of doors, especially one who was just two years old and alarmingly frail.

As a fresh gust swept the land Cindy Greerson scooped the little boy into her arms. From the bus stop to her home was a walk of almost a mile. No easy feat at this moment, even without the child to weigh her down. Yet as she held the little boy against her chest, the knowledge that he was sheltered from the wind was compensation for tired limbs.

The little fruit farm where she lived was at the end of a rutted sand road. As the wind grew stronger, and walking became more and more difficult, Cindy turned her eyes to a cottage midway up the road. For months it had been empty. Perhaps a door was unlocked or a window loose. If she could pause to rest, away from the wind and the dust it stirred up, the remaining walk would be easier.

Putting the child down for a moment, she opened a rusty-hinged gate. She was lifting Jeremy back into her arms when a movement caught her attention. A man was coming around the side of the house. For a moment Cindy stood quite still, rigid with shock. Almost as if she were in the grip of a nightmare she watched him approach.

At this distance she could not make out his face.

But she saw his height and the dark hair flung carelessly back in an impatient gesture, and the purposeful way of his walk. Only one man walked quite like that. Looked quite like that. Jason Peel.... It could be nobody else.

He saw her only seconds after she saw him. There was a momentary hesitation in the long-legged stride. He had recognized her, just as she had recognized him. Cindy did not need to see the expression in the dark intelligent eyes to know that. She saw him move, heard him call out, but the words he called were lost in the wind.

She did not wait to hear him repeat them. Grabbing Jeremy by the hand she fled through the gate. Fear and shock gave strength to weary legs so that she hardly noticed the wind as she covered the rest of the distance.

She was shaking as she closed the door of the farmhouse. She leaned back against it. Her eyes were closed, her heart was thudding; through her tired limbs a trembling had spread.

"Momma...momma....", A tentative hand pulled at her skirt.

For a few moments there had been only Jason and the violence of her shock. At the sound of the anxious voice she opened her eyes and looked down, almost as if she was surfacing from some pain-filled haze. The little boy was still tugging at her skirt. His eyes were wide and frightened, his voice urgent. It was as if the sight of his mother's

7

agitation plucked at his feelings of security. Cindy was swept by a wave of tenderness as she scooped him up once more and pressed his cheek against hers.

Apart from Jeremy there was nobody in her life. The little boy, with the tousled curls and the wide eyes so much like her own and the frailness that worried her so greatly, was the focus of all her love and purpose. Nothing and nobody else mattered. Least of all Jeremy's father—Jason Peel.

FOR ONCE IT WAS EASY to get Jeremy to bed early. Already the first drops of rain were falling with loud plops on the tin roof, and the wind howled through the trees. But the long bus ride into Durban and back had been hot and tiring, and the medical examination itself had provoked tears. By the time Jeremy had finished his drink, and then a boiled egg and a small slice of toast, his eyelids were beginning to droop.

It was raining quite heavily as Cindy finished the last of her chores. She went to the kitchen window and stared out over the orchards where mango trees bent to the wind. Normally this was a quiet time, the storm notwithstanding, a time of peace and serenity when she relaxed after the work of the day. Today she was filled with a restlessness that was compounded of many things: worry as to how she would cope with the exigencies of the months that lay ahead; anxiety for the child who lay sleeping in the next room; and a strange and nameless longing that was bound up with the man who, quite unbeknown to himself, was the father of the child.

For the first time since the shock of seeing the tall figure in the tumble of the cottage garden she could allow herself to think. To remember....

She had just turned eighteen when she went to the party given by Marlene's parents to celebrate their twentieth wedding anniversary. Most of the guests had been Marlene's parents' age, but Marlene, who had been allowed to invite a friend of her own, had asked Cindy to come.

For a while the two girls had stayed together, a little shy of the visitors who were all much older and more sophisticated than themselves. And then, quite suddenly, Cindy had seen him. He was very tall, lean and tanned. His hair was dark, and his face had a chiseled patrician look that set him apart from the other people at the party. He was talking to a very beautiful woman who seemed to be putting herself out to capture his attention. His head was inclined courteously as she spoke, yet Cindy sensed that he was impatient. There was a tautness in the long body, an aloofness in the polite mask of the face, that seemed to suggest that he wished very much to be elsewhere.

"Who is that man?" Cindy asked her friend.

"Jason Peel. The portrait painter." Marlene rolled her eyes in mock ecstasy. "Isn't he devastating?"

9

Devastating? Oh yes! In just a few seconds Cindy knew quite instinctively that he was devastating in more ways than Marlene could imagine.

"Pity he's so old. At least thirty." Marlene's interest, if it had in fact been that, quickly waned. "Let's go get something to eat."

"You go."

Still Cindy stood there, watching the man who was unlike anyone she had seen before. She was not a girl given to staring or bad manners, but there was a magnetism about Jason Peel that kept her eyes riveted on his face.

He looked up quite suddenly, so that she was caught off her guard. There were so many people in the room that she had thought herself unobserved. As his eyes met hers Cindy felt her body grow rigid and a rush of warm color flooded her cheeks. Later she would wonder why she did not look away, but at the time it was as if an invisible cord tied her eyes to his, forbidding them to shift their gaze.

His expression, even from a distance, seemed filled with an unusual probing. It was as if in just a few seconds he was able to take her measure. Cindy found that she could not breathe. And then, just as she thought she could not bear the intensity of the visual encounter a moment longer, she saw a lifting of well-shaped eyebrows and the slight curve of a smile at the corners of his mouth. The drama of the moment had passed, a moment so brief that the woman who had been talking to him had not even been aware of its existence.

Cindy turned and looked for Marlene. She was trembling, and she was not altogether sure why.

"Miss Greerson?" The voice was low and vibrant. It made no sense that she would know who the speaker was, and yet she did know.

She spun around, her eyes wide and a little frightened.

"You know my name," she blurted out foolishly, saying the first words that came into her head.

Amusement lighted the dark eyes. "It wasn't difficult to find out. I think you know mine?"

"Oh, yes." Again she had spoken too quickly. The color that came too easily flooded her cheeks.

"Can I get you something to drink?"

A drink was exactly what she needed. A glass to hold in her hands to hide their trembling. "A lemonade please."

She should have asked for something stronger! Would she never learn to say the right thing, she wondered miserably as she watched him walk toward the bar, a lithe figure with the graceful gait of a jungle animal. Jason Peel. She had recognized the name immediately. He was well-known in the artistic circles of Durban. Cindy had even seen some of his work. Now that she had met the man himself she knew that he was used to the company of beautiful and sophisticated women. The eagerness of the brunette who had talked to him earlier was evidence of that. To a man like Jason Peel, Cindy must appear young and naive and inexperienced. And she wondered why it mattered.

As she saw him coming across the room toward her she felt herself tense once again. *Show him that you're as sophisticated as anyone else*, she told herself firmly. Lifting her head, she tried a bold smile and wished that the pounding of her heart did not make the simple action so difficult.

She was searching a little desperately for something to say, when he said, "I want to paint you."

"Me?" She stared up at him in astonishment.

"You." He was watching her.

"But...." Confusion did away with the resolve to appear sophisticated. As conflicting emotions chased over her face it was easy to read. "I'm not beautiful."

"Not in the conventional sense," he agreed.

"In another sense?" she breathed.

Something flickered in the dark eyes, as if Jason Peel had had a glimpse of something he had never thought to see.

"In another sense," he acknowledged quietly. A finger went to her face, tracing very gently the outline of her eyes, then descending along the swell of a soft cheek to the corner of a sweetly tilted mouth. Cindy forced herself to stand very still. She waited for him to explain, but he did not.

The finger left her face and the hand dropped to his side. "Well, Cindy?"

How simply he had used her name for the first time. Natural enough, she was only eighteen after all, but how good it sounded coming from him.

"Well," he asked again, and she realized that she had not answered.

"If that's what you want," she managed, a little breathlessly.

"It is what I want." Dark eyes were steady.

She looked up at him. "When shall I come to your studio, Mr. Peel?"

"Jason," he told her. "And I don't want you in my studio yet, Cindy."

"Oh...!" She stared at him uncomprehendingly.

"I want to get to know you first." He paused, and as he studied her face she saw that his eyes were warm with laughter.

"I've seen the scared child," he went on with a perceptiveness that alarmed her. "And I've seen just a tiny glimpse of the woman. But I suspect that neither of the two is the real Cindy Greerson. It's the real Cindy I must know before I paint her."

So it had begun. In the month after the party Cindy saw him many times. At first she still felt the need to be something other than herself. When Jason took her dining she went to great pains with her appearance and tried to make worldly conversation over cocktails until he teased her out of her stiffness.

They drove to beaches outside Durban, where the sands were golden and deserted. They swam and sunbathed and went for long walks. In the evening they would return to the city, and Jason would find a casual place where they could eat and dance. He was a good dancer, rhythmic and supple. When he held her against him Cindy would feel a melting in her bones, and a great desire to be like this always, with her body pliant and soft against his.

She knew now that he wanted to do a series of portraits for an exhibition. She knew, too, that she loved him. The knowledge brought ecstasy, for she was experiencing emotions she had never dreamed possible. But it brought despair, also, for she knew that this magic time would come to an end when the portraits were finished.

For her the outings with Jason were times of love and enchantment. For him they were merely a means of getting to know his model. He was seeing her face in all its moods. He made her laugh, and sometimes the stories he told her brought tears. The long days on the beach, when she was clad only in a bikini, acquainted him with the shape and texture of her body.

They were dancing the first time he kissed her. She felt his lips in her hair, and as she pulled away to look up at him his mouth came down to hers. It was a gentle kiss, demanding no more than she might want to give. Yet despite her relative inexperience—Cindy had been kissed before, but only by

14

boys of her own age—she sensed a contained passion and wanting in the arms that held her.

It was very dark on the dance floor, so that Cindy was not inhibited as she put her arms around Jason's neck. She knew only that she wanted the kiss to go on and on .... She felt a tightening in the arms that held her, and then, as long-fingered hands moved over her back to her hips, the kiss hardened.

His mouth left hers at length to move softly over her face and down to her throat. Then as the music continued he buried his lips in her hair and held her close. Cindy's eyes were closed, her senses reeling as she felt the long hard legs move against her thighs, gently, yet with a sensuousness that was almost unbearable. The fabric of his jacket was rough against her cheek. Wanting to be still closer to him she nudged it open. Now against her cheek there was the silk of his shirt, and burning through it the warmth of his skin. Hardly knowing what she was doing she let her lips find a tiny gap between buttons, letting them rest against the roughness of a muscled chest. The action did not go unnoticed. There was a hissing intake of breath, and Cindy felt the strengthening beat of his heart against her cheek.

He did not love her. Could not love her, for she could in no way compete with the women of his world. But he was not untouched by her. The knowledge that she had stirred him, just a little, gave her a feeling of absurd satisfaction.

It was as if the night on the dance floor saw a turning point in their relationship. Now when Jason took her out Cindy did not feel that he saw her only as a girl he was studying for the purpose of painting her. There was a new tone in his voice when he spoke to her, a new expression when he looked at her—one that sent her pulses racing. He touched her more often, and each time he kissed her his embrace grew in strength, as did her own ardor.

She loved him so much now that she could not bear to think of a time when both the paintings and their relationship would end.

By now the sittings were in full swing. Twice a week Cindy made her way from her brother's home in Durban North to the house where Jason lived and worked. The house, which was built on one of the hills that surrounded the city, had a view to the distant sea. Only the studio had no sea view— Jason wanted nothing to distract him, he said—but it was a spacious room with big windows that let in the light.

John Greerson had objected at first when he had heard of the proposed sittings. Cindy's brother and his wife, Sally, had invited her to make her home with them after their parents had been killed in a car accident. It was a home where she knew that she was loved and wanted, yet as far as Cindy was concerned the arrangement could only be temporary. She was touched by her brother's concern—

he was ten years older than she was and seemed to feel responsibility for her welfare—yet she knew that she must make a life of her own; that she must be independent.

She overrode his objections regarding Jason. She had come to know the man she loved. It was true that in some ways he was still an enigma, but that was part of his fascination. One thing she did know: Jason would never do anything to hurt her.

She never grew tired as she posed for him, for she loved to watch him at his work. In his studio, with a sketching pencil in his hand and a sheet of paper before him, he was a different man from the exciting companion of the leisure hours. As she sat for him on a Friday afternoon, she marveled at his dedication. Against one wall of the studio were two portraits, almost finished. Both were commissions. All week Jason had worked on them, and on completion he would be well paid. And yet he still found time for more work. Cindy knew how much the approaching exhibition meant to him in terms of a purely personal satisfaction.

Now and then he looked up to note some detail of her appearance. Sometimes catching her glance he smiled, a smile that warmed his eyes and deepened the lines that ran from his nose to the corners of his mouth. And then he would bend to his work once more, and Cindy would know that his thoughts were wholly on the figure taking shape before him.

She did not mind. Later, when the light began to

17

fade, her time would come. They would leave the studio and go up to the kitchen and put out cheese and crusty French bread and a bottle of wine. They would sit close together, and when Jason's hand touched her it would be no longer the hand of the artist questioning a detail, but the hand of a lover.

Time had not dulled her awareness of him. With his head bent over his work it was safe to study him. Fawn trousers, tightly cut, emphasized the tautness of long legs, and the matching turtle-necked sweater revealed broad shoulders and a strong muscled chest. His hands moved deftly over the page. The same hands that could raise her to the very heights of happiness could also work magic on a blank page. Dark glossy hair fell forward over the wide forehead, to be thrust back now and then in an impatient gesture that was becoming rapidly characteristic. Cindy longed to thread her hands through that hair, but she forced herself to sit still. Much as she loved Jason, she was in awe of him still, and she knew that when he worked nothing else mattered.

She wondered sometimes if she would ever again meet anyone quite like him. The long fingers, the sensitive mouth and the eyes—those incredible eyes that could be alert and observant and compassionate and amused—all these were the marks of an artist. And yet he had other qualities, too, that, Cindy sensed, were usually to be found in men who lived the hard rigorous lives of the outdoors. The muscular figure gave off an aura of power and strength and confidence and something else; for lack of any other word she could only think of this quality as a sheer and virile maleness.

Many women would be drawn to Jason Peel. Despite her youth and inexperience Cindy knew that instinctively. But what kind of woman would Jason find attractive? And love...? Even the thought came out tentatively. What kind of woman would he love? For that woman would have to be very special, and to Cindy, who knew that she could never be that woman, the knowledge brought pain.

"Daydreaming?" He cut into her thoughts.

She had not even seen him look up. He was smiling. Cindy felt her heart go out to him. Sometimes her body grew a little stiff from sitting too long in one position, yet moments like these made her wish the sessions could go on forever.

"I suppose I was."

"Must have been something special." He was watching her, as if her answer meant more to him than the casual question implied. "Your face had a wistful look."

"A girl has her dreams," she laughed a little breathlessly.

His perceptiveness had been a little too close to the bone for comfort. She did not want him to guess her feelings. He would be embarrassed, and their meetings might come to a premature end. To change the subject she asked, "How is the work coming along?"

"Pretty well."

"May I see it?"

She knew the answer to that, for she had asked the question often before. Until now Jason had never been willing to let her see what he had done. There was no reason to suppose this time would be any different.

"If you like."

His voice was matter-of-fact, but as she looked at him she saw that the watchfulness had deepened, and in his eyes was an expression that sent her heart suddenly thudding. She did not move for a second. It was as if something momentous were about to occur. She was just a little afraid.

And then she knew she was being absurd. Her feelings for Jason endowed every word, every action, with an intensity of meaning that was not justified.

The soft green folds of the chiffon dress swirled gracefully against long slender legs as she leaped lightly from the dais. Jason stood waiting for her. As she came toward him he took a step sideways to make room for her.

The paper that lay on the drawing board was one of a series. Slowly, silently, Cindy glanced from one picture to the next, not quite believing what she saw, not quite understanding what to make of it. The girl in the pictures was very young, very vulnerable. In her expression was innocence coupled with a singular sweetness that gave an ethereal beauty to an appearance that was not, as Jason had said the first time they met, conventionally beautiful.

Was there a side to her nature that she had not fully recognized? Did it really exist? More important, was this how Jason saw her?

She turned to him, her cheeks warm with color, her eyes wide and green and filled with emotion. In his own face was a look she had never seen there before. Tenderness? Affection? Both of those perhaps—and something more?

There were questions she wanted to ask him. Questions relating to art, to its interpretation of personality. But as she opened her mouth to speak her heart was pounding so hard that the words did not come. Instead she could only say huskily, "Jason?"

"Cindy." The tone was quiet; there was no reason at all why the one word should have the sound of an endearment.

"You...you see me like that?"

"Yes, Cindy, I do."

Still the quietness of the tone, but in his face was a look of tautness, as if there was something he wanted, needed. Cindy could no longer think; she was only aware of her own emotions, her own needs.

"Jason...." His name came out on a broken

21

note as she leaned toward him. "Jason, please kiss me."

His lips came down on hers, gently at first and then with a growing firmness that called forth an answering response. Cindy's lips parted beneath his, willingly, eagerly, and her arms went up around his neck, her hands burying themselves in the luxuriant growth of hair at the top of his collar.

The arms that encircled her tightened, then loosened. Jason lifted his head. Cindy opened her eyes and stared up at him, puzzled, a little confused. In his face was a bleakness she did not understand. "Jason?" she whispered.

"Do you know how old I am?" he asked, a little fiercely.

"Thirty...."

"And you're eighteen. Just a child."

She understood then. She should have understood before. It was a child he had painted. The ethereal innocence in the pictures was that of a child. Ideal perhaps for his exhibition, but not for his lovemaking. When it came to love he wanted a woman.

But she *was* a woman. She had the emotions and needs of a woman. And more than anything in the world she wanted him to think of her as such. There was no embarrassment, no shame, as she pressed herself against him. She only knew that she had to prove something to him.

She heard her name emerge on a groan. And then his hands were clasping her shoulders, pulling her to him. As his lips touched hers once more the flame of pleasure cascading through her veins was a sweet torment. She arched toward him, the action quite instinctive.

She felt the hardening of his body as he molded her to him, soft feminine curves pliant against strong angular lines, as if they were meant to be there. He wanted her as much as she wanted him, she thought, and gloried in that knowledge. There was no gentleness now in the lips and tongue that tasted and tantalized and explored the softness of her mouth and the hollow at the base of her throat, pushing downward to nudge away the looseness of her dress in a search for her breasts. There was only passion and need that struck an answering chord within her. There was no rational thought now, there was just the knowledge that she loved this man and that she wanted to be close to him, part of him....

She did not resist as he slipped the dress from her shoulders and let it drop to the floor in a quick movement. She stood before him, rounded breasts firm and glowing in the late-afternoon light. She made no effort to shield her body with her hands. In his eyes was a silent adoration, and she was proud that he should see her as she was.

"Cindy...Cindy, you don't know what's happening."

Once more he stepped a little away from her, as if even now he had qualms.

"Yes...." No shame, just pride and exultation that he should see her as a woman.

"I'm a man, Cindy." His voice was ragged. "If I make love to you now there can be no stopping."

"I don't want to stop." Later she would wonder what had happened to all the principles she had been taught to hold dear. But this was no time for wondering. There was only love, and the aching need to express it.

From the studio to the bedroom was just one short flight of stairs. He picked her up and held her against him. As he carried her up her cheek was against his chest. He put her down on his bed and looked down at her. In the moment before he lowered himself onto her he said, "Don't be sorry, Cindy. Don't be sorry...."

Later, when they had slept and wakened and were starting to touch each other again, Jason said, "I have to know, Cindy, was this the first time?"

Such an odd note in his tone. She bent her head back a little to look at him. His eyes were hooded, hard to read. He was concerned, she thought on a new wave of tenderness, perhaps he thought he had hurt her. "It was the first time," she admitted.

She thought she heard him groan, but there was no time to wonder why, for then he was bending over her once more, and the pressure of his lips defied speech.

CHAPTER TWO

THE NEXT DAY was Saturday. As Cindy dressed for a modeling session she was slower than usual. Her limbs were filled with a feeling of languor, and when she looked into the mirror she saw that her eyes were infused with a radiance she had never seen there before. She had heard, but never quite believed, that love wrought changes in one's appearance. Now she was seeing the truth of it in her own image.

"Don't be sorry," Jason had said. She was not sorry. She would never be sorry. She could never regret something that had been quite so beautiful. She wondered if there would be a change in their relationship, whether Jason would refer to their lovemaking when she came into the studio, or whether he would settle down to work as if nothing had happened. She remembered the pictures he had drawn, the look of ethereal innocence. That look was gone now. Would he capture instead the new radiance, and would its appearance in the series tell its own tale?

She put on an outfit that Jason had not seen before—culottes of cream linen with a peach-colored top. The top was of a lacy, jersey knit fabric. The color enhanced the soft color in her cheeks, and the snug fit revealed the feminine curves of her slender figure. The green dress was still in the studio. She would change into it when she arrived.

There was a knock at her door. Then Sally's face appeared in the mirror. Her sister-in-law's brow was puckered in a slight frown, and Cindy thought she saw concern in brown eyes that were usually laughing.

She turned. "Sally?"

"Jason's here."

"Here?" Cindy was taken aback. "I was going up to the studio."

"He says he wants to talk to you. And to John." Brown eyes swept the younger girl's face, perceptiveness in the gaze that took in flushed cheeks and slightly trembling lips. "Cindy, is something wrong?"

Not even to Sally, to whom she was almost as close as she was to John, could Cindy relate what had taken place. There was no shame involved. There was just the knowledge, an ecstatic knowledge, that what had happened was between her and Jason. It concerned nobody else.

"Nothing's wrong." She smiled, and her sister-in-law drew in her breath at the flash of radiance in the green eyes. "I'll be ready in a moment."

Jason was in the living room. He was talking to John. Cindy thought her heart would stop when she saw him. He looked so tall, so distinguished. The thrust of his head was strong, his bearing vital. He was wearing navy slacks and a matching shirt, and the darkness of the clothes gave him an added litheness. Would she ever cease to be stirred by his maleness, Cindy wondered.

Her impulse was to run to him and to bend back her head for his kiss. But John's presence in the room called for decorum.

Both men turned at her entrance. There was seriousness in their faces. For the first time Cindy became aware of tension in the room, of a kind of hushed waiting. For no reason at all she found herself trembling.

"Sit down," John said, motioning to the two girls. As Cindy took a hard-backed chair—something told her she might need its support—she darted a glance at Jason. His answering gaze told her nothing. Her trembling increased.

"I want to marry you, Cindy." Jason came to the point abruptly.

Cindy stared at him, and as she stopped breathing for a moment the blood drained from her cheeks. Was this really happening?

"Cindy...?" She heard her name again, the sound seeming to come as if from a distance.

The color returned to her cheeks, and at the same time she found her voice. "Oh, yes! Oh, Jason, yes!"

A short silence greeted her words. For the first time Cindy became aware of the strangeness of the situation. The formality of the proposal, the presence of her brother and sister-in-law. Questioningly, apprehensively, she looked from one to another.

As if he read her thoughts John said, "Jason wanted Sally and me here—correctly." An enigmatic glance at the other man. "You are just eighteen, Cindy, and I'm your guardian."

All this formality was hateful. This was not how a proposal should be. Not when there was love, passionate love, between the two parties.

Only later would she remember that Jason had never said that he loved her.

She was about to open her mouth, to give some expression to her feelings, when John said, "You are very young."

She found her voice. "But I do know what I want." She looked at Jason. He was watching her, his face expressionless, his eyes unreadable.

"You could wait awhile...."

"No, John." She spoke with a new firmness. And then she was standing up and going to Jason. The arm that went around her gave her confidence. "I want to get married. Soon."

John and Sally left the room after that. Jason began to speak about the wedding and the life they would lead together, but for the most part his words washed over her. It was hard to concentrate on what he said when the reality of what had happened was still so new. Later he could say it all again.

For the present there was only a happiness like nothing she had known before. This man whom she loved so much that she had been prepared to make love with him even before marriage had been a possibility, had asked her to be his wife. They would share their lives, their hopes, their dreams. There would be nights of love and days of working together. The future seemed to stretch ahead, a haze of contentment.

"When shall we make it?" she heard him ask, and realized by his tone that he was repeating a question.

"Make it?" She looked at him as if through a blur.

"You haven't heard a word I've said, have you, darling?"

"Very little," she admitted, snuggling her head against his chest.

The arm that held her tightened. "I asked you when you want to be married."

She lifted her head and looked at him, her eyes wide and clear and certain. "As soon as possible."

The eyes that searched hers were oddly troubled. "You're sure of that? You wouldn't be able to have a big wedding."

"I don't need all the trimmings," she stated confidently. "Jason, darling, all I want is to be your wife."

The wedding date was set for two weeks later. Preparations began almost immediately. There was so much to do and so little time to do it. John was still hesitant about what he termed a precipitate marriage with a man so much older than herself. Sally, however, understanding Cindy's feelings, threw herself into the preparations with zest. Together they went into the city and bought the things Cindy would need. Jason insisted that he would give Cindy everything she could possibly want. But John took his responsibilities seriously and was obdurate. His sister would go into marriage with a trousseau.

In a shop in Durban's bustling West Street Sally spotted a roll of white satin embossed with tiny roses. The material was bought and taken home, and that night the wedding dress was cut out, and Sally and Cindy pinned and tacked far into the night. They could have gone into a shop and bought a dress. Making it together seemed to have more meaning.

As if he understood that her time was fully taken up, Jason called a pause in the portrait sittings. There would be all the time they needed once they were married, he told her. He came often to see her. Cindy wanted only to be alone with him, so that she could be in his arms. Such was the force of

30

his physical magnetism that she never grew tired of his kisses. If anything her ardor grew. But although he kissed her they did not sleep together again.

"Do you know what you're doing to me?" Jason asked once, when Cindy slid her hands under his shirt, pushing her hips up hard against his.

He was smiling, but the raggedness in his tone betrayed his need. Cindy never ceased to be astonished at her ability to arouse him. "Tell me," she teased.

"Witch." His lips found an earlobe and nibbled on the softness. "Two can play at that game."

"Why don't we?" There was only the raw desire of her body, the need to feel his body against hers, his arms, his chest, the flat stomach, the taut thighs.

"No." He put her firmly from him. "You're like a wanton little elf, my darling. But I have a few scruples left—at least where my future wife is concerned."

"You slept with me once," she reminded him curiously.

"That's true. But then I didn't know...." He paused and she saw the tiny frown in his eyes. "Just four days more, sweetheart." He grinned, the strong white teeth flashing wickedly against the tan of his skin. "Believe me, my darling Cindy, the waiting is even harder for me."

Four more days. And then only three. The days were busy but Cindy spent the nighttime hours in a kind of waiting. She was missing Jason. She wanted to be with him, next to him; wanted to be able to stretch out and touch the warm bare skin of the man she loved. But it was a happy waiting. Just three more days and then they would be together for the rest of their lives.

She was stitching the hem of her wedding dress when the doorbell rang. John was at work and Sally had gone out for the morning. Jason? No, Jason would be working, also. Marlene, perhaps? A little guiltily she realized how little she had seen of her friend since the night of the party. She would have to remedy that after her marriage. As she ran to the door she wondered who it could be.

A woman stood on the concrete step outside the door. A very beautiful woman with piercing blue eyes and a flawless complexion and black hair drawn back in a chignon. The picture of elegance, Cindy thought involuntarily, and pushed the ends of a shirt that had loosened from her slacks back into the waistband.

"Miss Greerson?" A cool smile revealed perfect teeth. "You *are* Miss Greerson? I wonder if I could have a word with you?"

"Won't you come inside," Cindy invited politely. And when the stranger was seated in the living room she said, "I don't believe we've met...."

"I didn't have to meet you." There was a blatant scrutiny in the woman's eyes that amounted to rudeness. Cindy felt a growing uneasiness. "The little innocent who let herself be seduced. You look the picture of the child Jason described.''

"You . . . you know Jason?''

"Evidently.''

"And he described me?'' Cindy's lips were suddenly very dry.

"With a certain amount of ironic amusement.''

"I don't believe you!'' Cindy burst out.

"Believe whatever you choose.'' She gave an indifferent shrug. "Keep on your rose-colored glasses if they will make you happier.''

Cindy's nails bit into the palms of her hands as she forced herself to remain calm. "I don't even know your name,'' she said quietly.

"Beulah Mason. Does that mean anything to you?''

"No.''

"It will.'' She spoke confidently. "You may never hear it from Jason's lips. He may be—'' she paused, a sly smile curving the perfectly painted lips "—too clever for that. But you'll hear it from others. In whispers. In laughter. Oh, yes, Miss Greerson, you'll hear it.''

"What are you trying to say?'' Cindy wondered how she managed to keep her composure. Inside her something very precious was crumbling, but she would not let the other woman know it.

"I'd have thought it was obvious,'' she commented with a brittle laugh. "Jason and I are lovers.''

"No!" The word was torn from pallid lips.

"Oh, yes, my dear. I'm Jason's mistress. Does that shock you?"

Jason and this woman with the hard eyes and the sneering mouth? Yes, it shocked her. It repelled her.

"It doesn't shock me at all." From somewhere Cindy found the strength to summon a quiet dignity she hadn't known she possessed. "I didn't expect Jason to be celibate. There had to be women in his life. But all that is over now."

Something flickered momentarily in the blue eyes that watched her. Admiration? Hardly. Surprise? Perhaps. Cindy didn't care. She had never met anyone she disliked more. She wanted the conversation finished and the woman out of the house.

"Over?" She said with a mocking drawl. "It's anything but over, Miss Greerson."

"You can't mean...." Composure deserting her, Cindy stared at the woman in shocked disbelief.

"Jason and I have a good thing going for us. A very good thing. Jason is an excellent lover. But then you know that already." Another laugh. "Or do you? Your experience—" there was a derogatory emphasis on the last word "—is so limited that you have no standard of comparison."

Cindy jumped from her seat. "Get out of this house!"

"When I've finished." Beulah Mason was unperturbed. "Tell me, Miss Greerson, does it mean anything to you to know that your husband will continue his relationship with me after your marriage?"

"He won't! Jason wants me. He loves me. That's why he asked me to marry him."

"Are you sure?"

Yes! The answer was on the tip of Cindy's tongue. But as something in the other woman's voice reached her, she bit the word back.

"What are you trying to tell me?" she asked at length, a little shakily.

"The truth." Beulah Mason's tone altered a fraction. "Don't you know why Jason asked you to marry him?"

"Because he loves me," Cindy said numbly. At the back of her mind registered the fact that he had never spoken of love.

"Perhaps that's what he would have you believe." Another appraisal from the icy eyes. "You are very young, Cindy Greerson, very innocent. I don't believe Jason has ever encountered someone quite like you. It's a great shame you had to meet up with him."

Get to the point, Cindy pleaded silently. *Say what you have to—what I have to hear at this stage, God help me—and then get out of this house, out of my life.*

"The night you spent with Jason was the first time for you, wasn't it?"

35

Cindy remained silent. But something in her eyes must have given Beulah the answer she needed. Her lips curved once more in a satisfied smile.

"Jason doesn't go for virgins, Miss Greerson. It isn't his style. When he found out that you had never slept with a man before he felt honor bound to marry you."

"No.... No, it wasn't like that." The protest emerged painfully from a parched throat. And then she asked, "Jason told you this?"

An evasive quality veiled the flawless face. Cindy was too stunned to notice.

"Yes," said Beulah Mason, after a pause that was only barely perceptible. "Jason told me."

Blindly Cindy turned to the window. Her eyes were blurred with unshed tears and her body was shaking. The part of her that could think and love and feel was filled with pain and an agonizing sense of loss. She did not even think of the impact that her obvious emotion would make on the watching woman.

A hand touched her shoulder. "You had to know, Miss Greerson. Just as you have to know that Jason will not stop seeing me."

"But...but we'll be married...." The lump in her throat made it hard to speak.

"He'll be tied to you by a piece of paper. He is tied to me by far more," Beulah said softly. "What can you offer him, Miss Greerson? An inexperienced child who knows nothing of the world. Jason's misplaced sense of honor won't stop him from being bored. With me he gets excitement, satisfaction, the lovemaking of a woman who knows what it's all about. You don't think he'll give that up?" The hand on her shoulder tightened. "Well, Cindy, will you still go ahead and marry Jason?"

Cindy turned, slapping the hand away. Her face was very pale. The tears were still massed behind her lids, but for the moment she had them under control. Her legs felt as weak as water, but she managed to stand very straight and very still.

"I owe you no answer," she said very quietly. "Whatever I do is between Jason and me."

"But—"

"That's all I have to say. Get out of this house, Miss Mason. Now!"

When the door had closed Cindy went to the window. Normally she enjoyed the view over the tropical garden and to the distant sea, but now she saw nothing of it.

She had to think. And think quickly. The wedding was only three days away. There was no time for uncertainty or indecision.

Had Beulah Mason spoken the truth? She was a hard woman, as cruel as she was beautiful. She had spared no punches and given no pity. Not that pity was something Cindy wanted.

She could talk to Jason, of course. In a way it was

the obvious course to follow. She could tell him what had happened, and together they could laugh it off. She loved Jason, and she trusted him. At least, she had trusted him until now.

If she was more certain of herself she would pick up the phone and tell Jason she had to see him. If only she knew that Beulah Mason's story was a fabrication. The woman would not hesitate to lie if that way she could benefit herself. But too much of what she had said, terrible as it was, had had the ring of truth. She had known so much. And how else could she have known it but from Jason himself?

For it was true that Cindy had been a virgin when she had let Jason make love to her. True that it was only thereafter that he had asked her to marry him. True that he had never said that he loved her.... It was also very obviously true that a woman of Beulah's undoubted charms and experience could offer a man of thirty something with which an inexperienced girl of eighteen could not hope to compete.

Cindy went to the phone. She lifted the receiver and began to dial the number. At the last digit she paused.

She could not talk to him now. If she tried she would break down. Jason would coax her out of her fears and the marriage would go ahead. But the doubts would still be there—the suspicions. Whenever Jason went out alone she would wonder where he was and with whom.

38

With trembling fingers she put down the receiver. She could not go through with it. When Jason heard her decision he might think she had been a coward. He would never know how hard the decision had been. He would be angry.

And then again perhaps he would not be angry at all. Perhaps he would be relieved. Cindy could only hope that the day would come when she, too, would be relieved that she had escaped from a marriage that would have been based on no more than a sham.

THREE WEEKS LATER Cindy discovered that she was pregnant.

Much had happened in that time. There had been the letter to Jason, telling him of her decision not to go through with the wedding. Jason's visit. He had been furious when she had declined to see him, not knowing that she could not trust herself not to break down in his presence. There had been John's anger and Sally's concern.

And there had been the decision to make a life for herself at Poinsettia, her parents' fruit farm on the Natal south coast. John and Sally had tried to talk her out of it. The farm was lonely, they said, and a little run-down, for their parents had lived in Durban and had farmed from a distance, and even now John, the executor of their estate, had been on the point of selling the place.

Her brother had not understood her need for a

place where she could lick her wounds and come to terms with what had happened. It was also a place where Jason would never find her, for she had made it clear that he was not to be told her whereabouts.

Sally had been more understanding, but even she had felt that Cindy was wrong to isolate herself. Now and then Cindy felt her sister-in-law's eyes on her face, compassionate but questioning, also, as if Sally wondered if there was more to the affair than they had been told.

A part of Cindy longed to confide in the woman who had become the sister she had never had. But there was another part, a stronger part that insisted that she must cope with her problems on her own.

Her first reaction on learning of her pregnancy had been shock, panic—even some fear. Her first instinct had been to run to the people she loved— Jason, John and Sally.

But after the initial shock had begun to fade, she had known that she would turn to none of them. It was not hard to guess what Jason's reaction would be, Cindy thought. The streak of honor that had prompted him to propose marriage in the first instance would be even stronger now. For this was no longer just a case of a shattered virginity. The issue now was a baby, and he was its father.

In the first wave of shock it was that very realization that had been the solution. Jason would marry her after all. He would take care of her and the baby would have a father. It was only when she could think more logically that she remembered why she had escaped from the marriage. She could not live the rest of her life with the knowledge that the man she loved had married her only because he felt that he had had to. In that respect nothing had changed.

She decided to reveal nothing to John and Sally, either. At least not for the moment, for the truth could not be hidden forever from her family. With a streak of independence and stubbornness she had not known she possessed, Cindy resolved that she would make a life for herself and her baby. She would cope with whatever came along. She would *have* to.

And somehow she *had* managed. It had not been easy. There had been the money left her by her parents. Not very much, but with the proceeds of the fruit grown on the farm she had managed to get by.

Jeremy was two years old now. John and Sally, deeply hurt at first at having been kept in ignorance of her pregnancy, now loved their nephew dearly. As far as the village of Sea View was concerned, Cindy had been quite open. There were people here who had known her for years. If she had pretended to be a widow she would have had to assume a new name. This she had not wanted to do. She had been surprised at their acceptance of the situation.

Sometimes at night Jason appeared in her dreams. But even this happened less and less often. For now there was a new problem. A more serious one. Jeremy had been born with a spine defect. Not so grave that it could not be remedied, yet cause for concern. Cindy had known for some time that her little son would need surgery. The visit to the doctor today had brought the date nearer. Ideally the operation should take place within the next few months.

That meant money. Quite a lot of money. It was the one thing Cindy didn't have. She could not even approach John, for her brother had been through a bad time financially. If he knew of Jeremy's plight he would try to find a way to help. But Cindy did not want that, for such help would only be at considerable cost to her brother and his wife. Somehow, somewhere, she would have to find the money herself.

The tropical storm unleashed its fury on land and sea. The rain struck the earth in hard-driving swaths. Thunder bounced in the sky. And although the sea was at least half a mile distant, Cindy could hear the roar of the surf. The storm did not worry her. It was an almost daily occurrence at this time of the year. The fury was strong, it would also be brief. And when the storm had spent itself the sun would shine through the clouds and the land would have a newly washed freshness.

What did worry her was Jason's presence so close by. What had brought him here, she wondered. Not the knowledge that he would find her here, for she thought she had seen her own surprise reflected in the rigid lines of his body. There was no reason why Jason would wish to seek her out. Yet the mere fact of his presence posed one more problem.

Jeremy had been asleep for more than an hour when there was a knock at the door. Cindy stiffened. She did not need to ask who was there. She had been expecting him.

CHAPTER THREE

SHE OPENED THE DOOR. No word passed between them as they looked at each other. Unconsciously almost she had been preparing herself for this moment, and now that it had come she was glad of the support of the doorjamb at her back, for her limbs had turned to water.

His eyes were hard and narrowed as they held hers. There was steel in the long line of the jaw, cruelty in the tight set of the lips. He was dressed in dark trousers and a crew-necked top that revealed the breadth of shoulders and the strength of a chest she had seen many times in her dreams. He was lithe as a jungle cat, and even taller than she had remembered him.

Cindy was the first to break the silence. "Come inside."

His expression did not change as he followed her

into the farmhouse kitchen. "I was just about to make some tea," she said shakily, the words giving her something to say and to do. As she turned to the sink and filled the kettle she made a conscious effort to compose herself. She had not thought that Jason's physical presence still had the power to affect her quite as much as it did.

There was just so much time she could give to the kettle. Then she had to turn. He was standing by the table watching her. The room seemed small at once, dwarfed by his size. Dark hair clung damply to the proud patrician head, evidence that he had spent some time outside in the rain; a strand of it fell forward onto the wide forehead, and he pushed it back with the impatient gesture she remembered so well.

"Shall we sit?" Cindy asked at length.

"If you like," he replied negligently.

There were two wicker chairs in the corner of the kitchen. As they sat down Cindy caught a whiff of the potent male smell, clean and exciting, that had always been a part of Jason. Momentarily her senses were dizzied.

"It's been a long time," she ventured, when the silence had grown deafening.

"A long time," he repeated mockingly.

She flinched. The tone of his voice and the expression in his face revealed that he had forgotten nothing of what had happened. Once he had been furious. It occurred to her now that he might, also, not understanding the reason for her behavior, have been hurt.

"The kettle t-takes a long time...." A little desperately she searched for words.

"I can wait."

The words were clipped, precise. Had he always spoken quite this way, Cindy wondered. If he had she had not noticed it. And those lines around the eyes, were they new? And the sternness of the chiseled face, had that always been there?

Her searching eyes met his. They held just a moment, then dropped, unable to sustain his gaze. His hands were in his lap. She saw the long fingers, the sensitive fingers of the artist who had drawn a girl in the sweet flush of slumbering innocence. The fingers of the lover, who had found the secret parts of her body and had wakened her to an ecstasy she had never dreamed possible.

As if he was touching her now she could feel again the hardness of his body, an exciting hardness of narrow hips and muscled arms and taut thighs. How she had reveled in the feel of him. Did he remember, she wondered. Involuntarily her eyes lifted, and as she saw his expression she knew that he did remember.

There were things that had to be said. No way of getting around them. No John and Sally here at Poinsettia, who could tell Jason that she did not want to see him.

She took a deep breath. "I'm so sorry...."

A harsh laugh. "Who do you think you're kidding, Cindy?"

"I really am." Beneath the bitterness of his gaze her mouth went very dry. She curled her fingers into the palms of her hands to stop their trembling. "You...you must have been very angry."

"If I'd known where to find you I'd have quite cheerfully killed you," he said grimly. "Somehow I thought you were the one person who wouldn't let me down."

She swallowed. He didn't know that Beulah Mason had been to see her then, that much was obvious. And despite the fact that what the woman had said would go a long way to exonerate Cindy's own behavior, she could not bring herself to tell him of her visit. Even now the fact that Jason had been carrying on an affair with another woman at the time of their engagement caused her pain.

"I'm sorry," she repeated. "I...I don't know what else I can say."

"Nothing," he advised crisply. "There's no way you can excuse what you did."

Silence followed his words. After the bitterness of his reproach it was not possible to launch into small talk. Cindy heard the whistle of the kettle with relief.

When she had given him his tea and taken a cup for herself she sat down again, first moving her chair just a fraction farther from his. So acutely aware of him was she in the silent farmhouse kitchen that she was certain that he must hear the thudding of her heart.

She took a sip of the tea to wet her dry lips. Then she asked, "Why are you here, Jason?"

"To paint."

She stared at him disbelievingly. "You've a commission for a portrait in Sea View?"

"No commission." His gaze raked her insolently in an open and detailed study that started at her face and progressed down over the rest of her body. As the warm flush flooded her cheeks Cindy knew that he was remembering the times when she had sat for him in his studio. "I want to try a new field."

"The sea?"

"Perhaps."

"You didn't need to leave Durban for views of the sea."

"No," he agreed.

Silence again. There was a brooding look in his eyes, and his brow was wrinkled in a frown. Cindy had always possessed some sixth sense where Jason was concerned. Instinctively she guessed what was coming. In an effort to forestall him she said, "Of course, Durban is a big city and here you'll find unspoiled countryside. There are such pretty beaches. And you'll just love the dunes. They're quite golden. And the palms—"

"Skip the commercial," he interrupted her savagely. "I want to know about the child."

Her heart missed a beat. "The child..." she faltered.

"The little boy." His eyes had completed their scrutiny of her body and had risen once more to meet hers. "He's yours, Cindy?"

"Yes, Jeremy's mine."

Her hands were still in her lap, clenched to stop their trembling. He reached for her left hand, forcing the fingers to uncurl, and turned the hand palm downward. There was nothing loverlike in the gesture, nothing gentle or tender. Nothing to justify the tremor that shot through her arm at his touch. He looked at the hand a long moment. When he released it the movement was so abrupt that the hand fell to her side like some inanimate object over which she had no control.

"You're not married." His voice was flat.

She shot him a quick look. "No...."

"And you weren't married when the baby was conceived."

It was a statement, not a question.

"No." She said the word proudly, though her lips felt numb.

"Jeremy is two years old, Cindy?"

She looked around her a little wildly, like a small hunted animal with no means of escape. "More or less," she managed.

"Near enough I should think." He ground the words out. "Is Jeremy my son?"

It was becoming increasingly hard to breathe.

49

The potent smell of his maleness was all around her, and vibrations seemed to spark and crackle in the confines of the small room. In Cindy's temples a hammer began a persistent knocking, and her chest felt tight.

"*Is* he my son, Cindy?"

Yes, she wanted to say, to scream, *of course he's your son, how else do you think I could have come by him? Don't you know that all the love that was in me exploded in our lovemaking the night this precious child was conceived?*

The words she wanted to say were written in fire upon her heart and her mind, but there was no way she would ever say them aloud. Blindly she shook her head.

The hand that reached for her chin was unexpected. She forced herself to sit very still as long fingers cupped her face and the thumb made a slow movement down her throat.

"I have to know, Cindy." He spoke very quietly now. "Even you must realize that."

The word "even" got through to her. Once he had thought of her as a naive child who had to be protected. Later he had taken her for a capricious teenager, a stupid girl who did not have the courage to follow through a commitment she had made. When had he ever thought of her as Cindy, a girl with a mind and a heart and values of her own?

Any interest he had shown in her had never

been for herself. Initially he had wanted to know her because he had seen something in her face that he wanted to capture on paper. In the same way his visit tonight had nothing to do with her, either. He had come because he had seen Jeremy, and he needed to know if the child was his son.

The answer came to her quite suddenly. She lifted her head and looked at him. The eyes that met his were clear and steady. "Jeremy is not your son, Jason."

She heard his swift intake of breath. His face was very pale. It was like a face carved of stone, pure and chiseled and honed down to the essentials. She had shocked him deeply.

"Who is Jeremy's father?"

There was no faltering in his tone, nothing to reveal that she had dealt him what was clearly a body blow. Jason was a man who could take punishment, Cindy thought, and felt a strange flaring of pride. Then she pushed the emotion from her. She could not let herself feel anything just now. She had to be on her guard. The interrogation was not yet over.

"Well, Cindy?"

"His name was Andrew." Strange how the name flashed through her mind as quickly as the rest of the falsehood.

"Andrew...?"

"Andrew Smith. The only man I've ever loved."

"I thought you loved *me*, Cindy." No emotion

in his tone, just the expressionless probing.

"For heaven's sake!" she said with a brittle laugh. "We never spoke of love, Jason. You never said you loved me. And...and I didn't say I loved you."

"You didn't need to say it. Your body said it all for you."

There was fierceness in the dark eyes. Cindy looked away. There was a limit to her acting ability. "That was just sex," she managed blithely. "You didn't think there was anything else, did you?"

"You little bitch!" he ground out, seizing her wrist in a grip of steel. "You wanton little bitch."

"You had your women," she flared at him, knowing she was playing with fire yet unable to resist. "Was there one standard for you and another for me?"

"I was thirty," he said harshly. "You were eighteen. You had the face of an angel. And I, God help me...." He stopped, a strange expression in his face.

"You what...?" She could hardly breathe as she waited for his answer. If he were to say, even now, that he had loved her, she would tell him the truth.

"It's unimportant." The expression had left his face, and his voice was cold. "You had me fooled, Cindy Greerson. You'd better tell me the rest."

"Perhaps it would be better if we changed the subject." The fire had gone out of her. She felt drained and cold. The last thing she wanted was to elaborate on her impulsive untruth.

"We'll do nothing of the kind." The grip on her wrist tightened, his fingers biting cruelly into the softness of her skin. "Start talking."

This was a new Jason, with the hateful coldness in his eyes and the arrogant tilt of the head. The depth of his anger fueled similar feelings in Cindy. What right had he to judge her? His own behavior was suspect, though he did not know that she knew it.

"His name was Andrew," she began in a small tight voice. She paused for a moment to gather her thoughts, then turned a little in her chair, so that her eyes were concealed in the shadow of long thick lashes. It would hurt her to tell this story as much as it would hurt him to hear it.

"Go on." It was a dry command.

"I met him a few months before I met you. I fell in love with him. I loved him totally, absolutely."

She paused once more, and ventured a glance at Jason's face. His eyes were hooded, making it impossible to assess his reactions. Only the tightness of his jaw and the pallor around his nostrils revealed that what she was saying meant anything to him.

"You slept with him?" he asked quietly, the very quietness giving the words a dangerous quality.

She lifted her chin. "Many times."

The tension in the room deepened. It was almost

possible to hear the currents that trembled between them.

"You little tart," he said in disgust.

In spite of herself she flushed. "Because I tell the truth?"

"I would have understood the truth if you'd told it to me at the beginning. You're not the first girl to have an affair. I wouldn't have condemned you for that. But no, you were the innocent virgin—the sweet young girl."

His eyes traveled derisively over her, making no secret of his contempt. "You did not resist when I made love to you. In fact you seemed to want it as much as I did. I thought afterward that you'd been overcome by the strength of your emotions. You must have laughed at me for a fool."

Was this all that remained of the magic that had been with them that night? She had thought then that she would never regret what had happened between them. It had been a thing of such love and beauty, that all her moral principles had been swept away. Little had she imagined this aftermath of anger and contempt.

"Why did you do it?" He was still watching her, savagely, as if he wanted nothing more than to tear her apart and punish her. "You say you were in love with this Andrew. Why did you want me, as well? Is there an alley cat behind that sweet exterior? Or did you just want to add a rather well-known scalp to your list of conquests?"

She had not imagined that he could be quite so brutal. Angry, yes. Hurt and letdown. But this deliberate cruelty was a side of him she had not suspected. Pain twisted inside her, but added thereto was pride and an anger of her own.

"I was pregnant," she said, very deliberately.

"Had Andrew let you down?"

"Andrew would never have let me down. We planned to get married. He...he was killed in an accident."

Odd how easily the lies came after the first one. She stared out of the window, forcing herself to be calm. The onslaught was far from over. Somehow she had to be strong enough to see it through to its end.

"So," he drawled ominously, "you had to find yourself another man. And quickly."

She turned from the window and slanted him a provocative glance from beneath her long lashes. "Precisely."

"What made you think I'd play ball, Cindy?" His tone was even, but she saw the incredulous fury in the narrowed dark eyes, the tautness of the skin that seemed stretched tighter than ever over his cheekbones.

"I took you for a man of honor," she said lightly over the lump at the back of her throat. "You thought that you'd robbed me of my virginity, that therefore you were duty bound to marry me."

A little breathlessly she waited for him to deny

55

the one fact that had haunted her for almost three years. As she watched him she saw something come and go in the dark eyes. *Deny it*, she pleaded silently, *deny it, and perhaps we can make a fresh start.*

Unexpectedly he smiled, a lazy smile that curved his lips but did not reach his eyes. "Well thought-out, my dear Cindy. Just one thing puzzles me. Once you'd caught me, why did you let me go?"

The pain was more intense now. Beulah Mason had spoken no more than the truth. Otherwise he would have denied it.

"I couldn't go on." Her voice was very low now. It was becoming more difficult to speak.

"Don't try to tell me you were afflicted by sudden scruples," he threw at her derisively.

"Yes!" She flung her head back, her eyes wide and clear and very bright. "But not as far as you were concerned, Jason. Only for Andrew.... I realized that...that I still loved him too much to...to be able to marry anyone else."

There was a moment of intense silence. Cindy sat at the edge of her chair, every nerve tensed.

"Why didn't you have the courage to tell me? You owed me that much. Instead you sent word that the wedding was off. I came to see you—did you know? And John said you wouldn't see me. Did your brother put you up to the whole thing?"

"No." Urgently she turned to him. "John had nothing to do with it. Please, Jason, you must believe me." She put her hand on his arm. "Jason...."

He shook off her hand in distaste, as if some part of him had been soiled. "You can't expect me to believe anything you say, Cindy. Even you can't be quite so naive."

"It's true, though." Her voice was thick with unhappiness. "John didn't know about the baby." And then, uncertainly, she said, "Jason, I'm sorry...."

"Sorry!" he exploded.

In one swift movement he was out of his chair. For a terrible moment he towered above her, dark and furious, like some ancient god of the night. And then he had yanked her to her feet and was crushing her against him. His hands were on her hips, pushing her tight against his own hips and thighs, and through her outrage she could feel the muscled hardness of his body. She tilted her head to look at him, so that she could voice her displeasure. But the words dried in her throat. She could see only the rigid line of his jaw and the sweep of his neck and the sensual shape of his lips. Against all logic she waited for the lips to descend to hers.

He did not kiss her. She heard a mirthless laugh somewhere above her head, and wondered if he guessed at the flames of desire that coursed through her body. Even now....

As suddenly as he had grabbed her he let her go. He seemed to push her from him. The movement was so abrupt just when her limbs had gone weak, that she fell backward against the wall.

He did not help her up. Once she had thought him compassionate, but there was no compassion left in him for her. She was still crouching against the wall when she heard the door slam behind him.

For a long while she stayed slumped against the wall, just as he had left her. She was very cold, drained and numb, and a great trembling attacked her limbs.

She had known from the moment she had seen Jason that he would come. She had guessed that he would be bitter and accusing. But she had not thought that the meeting would be quite so traumatic.

It was almost three years since she had seen him, and she had hoped that her feelings for him had faded. In the space of no more than half an hour that hope had been dashed. For she could not deny to herself the feverishness of her response. Even when he had taken her wrist in a vise of steely anger, mixed in with her own anger had been an exultation that boded ill for the future.

She could only hope that Jason would decide to vacate the cottage long before his lease was up. He was rich enough not to notice any money he would forfeit. And surely their meetings—inevitable as they lived so close to each other—could only bring them both more bitterness.

She got up at length and put on the kettle once

more. She was so cold that she had a great need for a warming cup of tea. While she waited for the water to boil she went to Jeremy's room.

The little boy was sleeping. He had slept right through the meeting with Jason, and for that she was thankful. He was too young to understand what was said, but he was alert and sensitive, and the poignancy of the atmosphere and the nuances of tone would have got through to him. He would have been upset as much by an atmosphere that he could not understand as by the roughness to which Jason had subjected her.

Jason.... Jeremy's father, though neither of the two would ever know it. Jeremy Greerson was the name by which he went in the village. It was his legal name. Jeremy Peel would have been his name if his parents had married; if Beulah Mason had not come upon the scene in time to tell his mother the truth.

The night-light was on in the room. As Cindy looked down at her son she thought he looked even frailer than usual. Long silky lashes cast a shadow over the soft baby cheeks, and a lock of fair hair lay over his forehead. The hair was a few shades lighter than Cindy's own; with the years it would darken to the same rich color.

Gently she brushed the hair back from his forehead before bending to kiss him very lightly. Tenderness welled inside her. She had never imagined that she could grow to love her child quite so much. When she had learned of her pregnancy she had been too shocked to think of the actual child that would enter her life. Pregnancy had been a fact, a not very palatable fact, that she had had to adjust to. Dimly she had known that she would keep her baby and bring it up as best she could. At a later stage in her pregnancy, when it had no longer been possible to keep it a secret from her family, John and Sally had offered to adopt the child and give it a home. This she had refused.

What she had not foreseen was the depth of love that would come with Jeremy's birth. It was hard to think that there had been a time when she had dreaded his coming. He had become the most precious thing in her life.

She kissed him again. This time her touch must have got through to him, for he stirred and muttered. His hand flung up across his face, and his lips curved in a momentary grimace. The grimace was Jason. For a moment the resemblance between father and son was so striking that Cindy caught her breath.

A casual observer would see no similarity between Jason and Jeremy. Where Jason had dark hair and a near-swarthy complexion, Jeremy was more like his mother. For that Cindy was grateful. She did not want Jason to recognize that the baby was his. For the moment he believed in the fictitious Andrew. Let him once suspect the truth and he would be hard to deal with. He would want some right to the child who was his son.

He would want a say in his future. Especially in his immediate future. His health and the operation that lay ahead....

For the first time Cindy wondered if she was doing the child an injustice. A child needed a father. There were circumstances when this was not possible. But such was not the case in this instance. Jason had wanted to marry her. He might still want to marry her, Cindy suspected, if he knew that he was Jeremy's father.

In fact, he might insist on marrying her, and though the procedure would be no less a sham now than it would have been almost three years earlier, Cindy knew that her defenses were at a low point. Jeremy's health was a very real worry. The operation had been on her mind for some time, but today's visit to the doctor had brought it much nearer. In her need for security and for the necessary money she might well agree to something that she would later regret.

Green eyes were troubled and thoughtful as they studied the sleeping child. Was she selfish in not telling Jason the truth? Was she putting herself before Jeremy in not wanting to be married? Was there something wrong in not wanting marriage without love? For Jason had never loved her. She had loved him once, very much, but that love no longer existed. True, her senses still leaped at the sight of him. He had only to touch her to provoke an immediate response. But the response was purely a physical thing, a matter of sheer chemistry. It did not, *could not*, have anything to do with love.

That being the case, surely Jeremy could not hold it against her that she had deprived him of a father. He would not be happy in a home in which the atmosphere was sterile, in which warmth and love and companionship were absent. Jeremy's most pressing need at present was an operation. For that money was needed, and somehow she would find a way of getting that—though she still had no idea how.

But two things were clear: she would raise the money, and she would not marry Jason for the purpose. On no account must Jason find out that Jeremy was his child. She had made her way until now and would continue to do so, even if that meant adhering to the story of the fictitious Andrew.

CHAPTER FOUR

IT WAS ONLY AT THE THIRD KNOCK that Cindy came out of her reverie. As she went to the door her mind flew to Jason. She was not ready to see him again.

But it was not Jason who looked down at her questioningly. For a moment she stared bemused into the smiling eyes of Graham Langley, the young vet who was her closest friend.

"You look as if you've seen a ghost," he said.

"Oh, no." She tried to speak lightly. "Come in, Graham."

"I said I'd call in on my way home from my rounds. Did you forget? You weren't sleeping?"

"No...no, of course not. I guess I didn't expect you quite so late." She was hunting for words, trying to restore a semblance of normality to her manner.

"I'd have been here earlier if Mrs. Van Vuuren's cow hadn't taken so long over calving." And then, as he noticed her pallor, "Cindy, something *is* wrong."

"No, really. Let me make you some tea."

"I'd like that," he said gratefully. "You took Jeremy to the doctor?"

"Yes. He will have to have the operation."

"Soon?" Brown eyes were warm with concern.

"A few months."

"No wonder you're so pale." He was beside her in an instant. As his arm closed around her shoulders Cindy leaned her head against his chest. There was comfort in his strength.

"I knew it was coming, but it was a shock all the same," she acknowledged.

"It must have been." After a moment Graham asked, "Did he mention money?"

"Yes."

"And that's worrying you, too, isn't it?" he asked perceptively.

"Yes." She lifted her head and looked at him frankly. "But I'll manage."

"You'll speak to your brother?"

"No...." Her eyes were troubled. "Not unless I absolutely have to."

The hand on her shoulder tightened. Even as she guessed what was coming, Cindy marveled that one man could stir her senses to a wild frenzy where another provided no more than a very welcome reassurance.

"Cindy...sweetheart, I want to ask you again—"

"No, Graham." She pushed herself a little away from him. The eyes that met his were warm and steady—unafraid.

"Yes! You know I want to marry you. I don't have much money, but maybe somewhere...somehow...." His eyes darkened. "At least I'd have the right to help you."

It was not the first time Graham had asked her to marry him. And more than once Cindy had been tempted to accept. Life with Graham might never be exciting. It might never contain the passion she had experienced only once. But it would be peaceful and harmonious, and would bring its own kind of happiness. Cindy thought sometimes that she had never met a person she liked more than Graham, with his steady warmth and open manner. Drawn to him as she was, there had been times when she had been very tempted to agree to his proposal. Yet always something had kept her back. Each time the image of a tall dark man with a lean sculptured face had inserted itself between Cindy and her means to happiness.

This time the temptation to say yes was stronger than ever. Graham was fond of Jeremy. He had never pressed her for details of the child's birth and would look upon him as his own son. It would not mean an end to her financial problems, but spiritually and emotionally Graham would be the support she needed in the months to come.

Regretfully Cindy pushed temptation from her. Graham would never know quite how appealing his proposal had been. But after what had happened with Jason today she had to do a lot more thinking.

"Dear Graham," she said gently. "You are always so kind to me."

"Kind!" Brown eyes clouded with frustration. "I love you, Cindy. Don't you understand?"

"I...I do," she said shakily. "But I can't.... Please, don't press me."

"If there was someone else I could understand." He stared down at her, puzzled. "But you live here all alone. There's nobody in your life. At least not that I know of. Don't you want to get married?"

"One day, perhaps." And then, before he could make something of that, she said, "Tell me about Mrs. Van Vuuren's cow. I thought she had passed beyond the age of bearing calves."

Graham talked a few minutes about the cow that had surprised both its owner and himself. He made the anecdote purposely light and amusing, and was gratified when a smile chased some of the worry from the sea-green eyes. They drank tea together and talked a little more about Jeremy. At length he looked at his watch and stood up to go.

He was at the door when he said, "I saw a light in the cottage down the road. Did you know it had been let?"

"I just heard today." The words came out too quickly.

He shot her a perceptive glance. "You've met the new tenant?"

"Briefly." She hesitated, cursing the color that flooded her cheeks whenever she was stirred or embarrassed. "His name is Jason Peel. He...he's an artist."

"I see." He stood quite still, his gaze on eyes that had become a little too bright. At length he said, "You seem agitated. You've had some brush with the man?" And on a sudden thought, "He couldn't have made a pass at you?"

"Gracious no!" The words were a little too close to the truth for comfort. "It's just.... Well, it was a bit of a shock seeing him so suddenly."

A new expression appeared in the pleasant face. "You knew Mr. Peel from before?"

"We'd met."

Leave it at that, she pleaded silently. *I can't talk about it. Not now. Perhaps never.*

Graham was still watching her, his eyes alert and narrowed. It was clear that he registered her distress and that there were questions he wanted to ask. And then, with the tact that she had observed in him so often, and that was so much a part of his warmth and appeal, he leaned toward her and pressed his lips briefly against hers. "Have an early night, sweetheart," he said lightly. "I'll call in tomorrow if there's time."

Cindy lay sleepless a long time. Her limbs were heavy and her head was aching as she switched off the light and slid between the sheets. Sleep had never seemed more inviting. But oblivion was not possible when thoughts and images chased in her mind. So much had happened in just a few hours. So much lay ahead.

Jeremy's operation had become a reality. It was something she must cope with—on her own, and soon.

Jason's presence was no less real. That, too, she must cope with. Also in her own way.

Intellectually she knew exactly what she had to do. She must remain aloof, polite but unyielding. Show no hint of emotion or softness. She must be the mature woman he would expect to find three years after knowing the innocent girl.

Emotionally she hoped she was capable of playing the part. There had been moments today when her body had shown all its old signs of betraying her. The grip on her wrist had produced a tingling that she had been unable to quell. When he had pulled her up against him, so that his hips and thighs had strained against hers, flames of desire she had hoped were dead had coursed through her veins. Jason had acted only in anger, in punishment, perhaps. But her treacherous body had responded as if to a lover's caresses.

If only it were possible to marry Graham. She could say the word and he would arrange to have the banns read. He had made his feelings clear more than once. But she could not do it. At least not until she knew she was being fair to him. And, whispered a tiny voice deep inside her, when she knew she would also be fair to herself.

Jason's image swam into her mind, lean and gaunt and mocking; aware of the distress he had caused her and gladdened by it. With a little cry of pain Cindy jumped from her bed and ran to the open window, where she took long calming breaths of the fresh night air.

The storm had long since subsided, and the sky was cloudless once more. The air was heavy with the scents of ripening fruit, mingled with the sweetness of the jasmine and frangipani and poinsettia that grew outside the window. Somewhere a frog croaked its nightly song, and in the distance a dog barked. In the background, reassuring in its constancy, was the sound of the sea.

Poinsettia was home. It had been a transitory kind of home when Cindy was a child and her parents had traveled out from Durban on weekends; it was a permanent one now. Three years ago she had seen it as a refuge, a haven where she could pick herself up and start life anew. She could not let that refuge be torn from her. Somehow she must see to it that Jason—whose stay in the cottage could only be temporary—was not allowed to disrupt her life again.

SHE WAS WORKING in the orchards next morning when Jason arrived. Jeremy was kicking a ball on the ground, gurgling with pleasure each time his foot sent the ball rolling down the sandy incline. Already the sun was high in the sky, and the heat was burning through their thin clothing. Cindy paused, and as she drew a hand across a moist brow she watched the little boy. His laughter brought an answering smile to her own face, but mingled therewith was sadness. Impulsively she bent down and hugged him to her.

A long shadow formed on the ground. Cindy looked up quickly, stifling an exclamation.

"Jason!" Letting go of Jeremy she stood up swiftly, smoothing her shirt into the waistband of her denims.

"Hello, Cindy." And then, inclining his head toward the little boy, "And this, I take it, is Jeremy." His tone was devoid of warmth.

"Who dat?" Jeremy's face was puckered, as if he sensed aloofness in the man who looked down at him.

Looking from one to the other, Cindy was struck by the likeness. Both were frowning, an expression so similar that it pronounced them father and son. A wave of panic swept her, but she pushed it down firmly. There was no danger that Jason would see what she saw. Jeremy's features and coloring were her own. Only a discerning and objective spectator—

which Jason was not—would pick up the subtle similarities of personality and expression.

"This is Mr. Peel," Cindy said carefully. Graham was Uncle Graham, but she could not see Jason fitting quite so casually into an assumed relationship. Nor did she want him to. "Say hello, darling."

"No like Peel." A small bottom lip pushed out mutinously. Jason did not pout. When he was angry his lips tightened. Yet again there was a similarity that under different circumstances would have made Cindy laugh.

Unexpectedly Jason grinned. The flash of white teeth against the tan of his face was so striking that it sent the blood racing through Cindy's veins. "Sorry about that, Jeremy," he observed. "Liking our fellowmen is not always easy."

This was so much above the child's head that he went back to his ball, leaving his mother to contend with Mr. Peel alone.

Her pulse still had not settled back to normal. Despite her resolve of the previous night, it was no easy matter to remain immune to Jason's virile vitality. He was wearing jeans today, the fabric clinging tightly to the long legs. A sports shirt, the top four buttons of which were open, revealed a bronzed torso, and from the top of the collar thrust the strong column of his throat. His eyes were dark, alert and intelligent, and his face had a fresh glow as if he had just returned from a swim. If Jason had spent any sleepless hours last night there was certainly nothing to indicate as much.

"Working?" he asked.

"As you see," she said coolly. "We've nothing to say to each other, Jason. I'd prefer it if you left."

There was a brief flicker in the dark eyes. He was watching her, his expression sardonic, the gaze that lingered on her body as blatant as to be insulting.

"I came for a purpose."

"If it's sugar you want, there's some in the kitchen," she said very politely, then stooped to pick up her rake.

She was unprepared for the hands that gripped her shoulders, pulling her up and around. "This new caustic manner doesn't suit you." His voice was hard. "What happened to the sweet Cindy I once knew?"

His nearness was so devastating that it sent her heart thudding hard against her ribs. It was an effort to keep herself from weakening. "She no longer exists."

He held her a moment longer, the long fingers biting into her flesh with a fierceness that hurt. It was as if he was containing an anger that sought to punish her more than civilized behavior would allow.

"You said you had a purpose," she goaded.

"Yes." His voice was dry. "I want to paint you."

He was joking, of course! He had to be! She threw back her head to look at him. The eyes that met hers were steady, sardonic still, but coupled with an enigmatic expression she did not understand and that made her uncomfortable.

"You...you can't mean it," she said, suddenly uncertain.

"I mean it."

If only he would let go of her shoulders. His touch made it hard to think. It was quite impossible to think when her heartbeat was so loud that she could hear it. Yet think she must, for Jason's request smacked of a trap.

"Yesterday you intimated you were going to do landscapes."

"I'm capable of working in more than one field. Well, Cindy?"

"You painted me once." Her voice was very low.

"An unforgettable experience."

Wincing at the mockery she forced herself out of his grip. "There's no reason why you'd want to do it again."

"Oh, but there is." His voice was very soft, very dangerous.

In spite of herself she was interested. "Jason...the way you depicted me then...that Cindy no longer exists."

The harshness of his laugh shocked her.

"Jason...."

"Let me explain." Still that softness. "The Cindy I painted three years ago was a beautiful girl. A virgin on the threshold of awakening—or so I

73

imagined. She had the face of an angel. I didn't know then that her soul was that of a wanton."

She should hit him, of course; very hard, right across his face. But something kept her back. She had shocked him with her story of the fictitious Andrew. Shock? Perhaps it was no more than mere hurt pride. Now he was retaliating. If she kept very quiet and refused to rise to his baiting, he would go and she would be finally rid of him.

"Don't you want to know how I'd paint you now?"

Later she would wonder how she could have fallen into his trap. But for the moment her curiosity was stronger than her caution. "Well?"

"As a street girl." One hand left her shoulder and pushed aside the top of her shirt to let the fingers trail suggestively along the curve of a breast. "As a beautiful girl of the night."

"You swine!" she lashed out at him, jerking away from him.

"Momma?" Jeremy ran up curiously, caught by the unusual vehemence in his mother's tone.

"It's nothing, darling." She struggled to make her voice calm. "Go and play." And then, turning back to Jason with her voice low this time, she hissed, "You rotten bastard! Get off my farm or I'll lay a charge against you."

"As you like." He stepped away from her, his movements unhurried. "If you decide to change your mind you know where I live."

74

It was as well that he went when he did. Tears had gathered behind her lids, and she did not want him to see them. Angrily she brushed them from her cheeks as she saw him vanish through the trees. No matter what he thought of her, nothing gave him the right to behave as he did. "If you change your mind ..." he had said. She would *never* change her mind. Not in a million years. If he thought she would sit for him again he would wait a long time.

There was work to be done. More than ever she needed to work. The fruit was ripening and she could not afford helpers. *Damn you, Jason Peel,* she cursed as she went back to what she had been doing before he arrived. *Damn you for coming here to destroy the serenity and contentment that took me so long to acquire.*

For a while all her movements were jerky. Now and then she ripped a mango from a branch with unnecessary force, tearing at the velvety skin. Slower ... she had to work more slowly, to regain some modicum of calm. Finally she managed it. But as her hands moved over the fruit with just the right speed, her mind was far away. Somewhere deep inside her there were still tears. She was weeping for a love that had once been only beauty. All that was left of it now was ugliness.

The morning wore on. The sun climbed higher in the sky. It grew hotter and still hotter. The humidity, always strong in this part of the land, was so heavy that it was hard to breathe. Occasionally

75

Cindy paused, wishing for a breeze to cool her fevered skin.

Jeremy had grown very quiet. Earlier he had been playing. Now he leaned lethargically against the trunk of a tree, all the energy drained from the small frail body. A chill snatched at Cindy's heart as she looked at him. For the last hour she had been so concerned about what had happened between Jason and herself that she had spared no thought for her child. Jason was in the past, she told herself fiercely. He had no place in her life, in her thoughts. The fact that he was Jeremy's father counted for nothing and she was more resolved than ever that he would never know it.

It was a waste of precious energy to think of Jason. She must concentrate her thoughts on Jeremy. What was important was the operation he needed to restore him to full health and the money to make that possible.

She had vowed that she would have that money. Had told the doctor so. Words spoken in desperation and hope and bravado. At this moment, dispirited and tired, the prospect of finding that money seemed totally remote.

Yet she must find it. She must. Jeremy *must* have the operation. Somehow there must be a means of getting it. Short of asking Jason for it. For he would give it if he knew that Jeremy was his son. Yet it was the one thing she could not do. The *only* thing she would not do.

76

Jason.... The idea came to her slowly. Seemingly from nowhere. As it registered in her conscious mind she stood quite straight, quite still, a bemused expression in the wide green eyes that stared at the inert body of the child.

The idea was impossible. Or was it...? Had she not resolved that there was *nothing* she would not do?

Of course Jason might say no. It was a possibility she must face. But there was just a chance that he might say yes....

She left the orchards a little earlier that day. When she had given Jeremy a snack of sandwiches and a glass of freshly squeezed orange juice, she phoned Mrs. Langley, Graham's widowed mother. That lady, elderly and with some time on her hands now that Graham was the only one of her family still living at home, had developed a great fondness for Jeremy and was happy to look after him if Cindy needed time to herself. When Cindy asked if she could bring Jeremy over for a while, there was an enthusiastic yes.

Leaving Jeremy at the Langley farm, Cindy hurried back to Poinsettia and her mirror. It was a long time since she had given her appearance much attention. Looking at herself now she realized that if three years had changed Jason, she had changed, too. The wide eyes had an expression that had been wrought by worry and pain. The skin of her face was soft still, but her cheeks no longer had quite the young-girl curve they had once had. Once her hair had been long and curling. Now it was kept short, both for coolness and so that it would not get in her way while she worked. She was no longer the dreamy innocent girl Jason had painted. But neither, she thought, was she totally unattractive. There had been men in Sea View, Graham in particular, who had made it clear that they were drawn to her.

Her appearance was not the only thing that had changed. Three years earlier she had been a girl on the threshold of life, dreaming and eager, trusting and open to the headiness of love and passion. Now she was a woman—mature, thoughtful and concerned with problems she had never anticipated. Some of her dreams had been shattered and with them some of her trust. She wondered if she could still love. Not the kind of loving that went with caring for a precious child, but the loving that could be awakened only by a man. She was not sure that she could. But she was still open to passion. That much her body had revealed to her the previous night. She would have to take care that Jason did not know it.

She glanced at her watch as she walked to the bathroom and turned on the taps. A shower and a shampoo. Then back to her bedroom, to stand perplexed before her meager wardrobe. At length she chose a pale pink halter-necked dress that she had worn sometimes on outings with Graham. The cut of the dress revealed smoothly tanned shoulders, and the skirt flared slightly from a trim waist. Her long tanned legs were bare, and on her feet were narrow-strapped sandals. She spent a few minutes brushing her hair, then applied the makeup she wore only rarely. Green eye shadow made her eyes deep and enormous, and a touch of coral lipstick emphasized the generous tilt of a curving upper lip.

Her heart was beating fast as she opened the gate that led to the cottage. Jason was nowhere in sight, but a long low gray car was in the garage. Unless he had gone for a walk he must be at home.

One deep breath for courage, then she put her finger to the bell. Panic rose in her throat as she waited. Only the thought of Jeremy kept her at the door when all her senses urged her to flee.

She was about to press the bell once more when the door opened. Jason looked down at her, his eyebrows lifted. He was wearing his working clothes—she knew them well. Once she had thought the paint-spattered shirt made him curiously vulnerable. Now she knew better. Vulnerability was surely not one of Jason's weaknesses.

"A neighborly visit?" he drawled. "Somehow I didn't expect it quite so soon."

His sarcasm did not make matters easier. She quelled the anger that rose inside her. Retaliation at this point would spoil everything. Wetting her lips, she forced a smile. "Hello, Jason."

He looked past her. "Where is Jeremy?"

"With a neighbor." She squared her shoulders. "Aren't you going to ask me in?"

With mock courtesy he stepped inside. In the living room Cindy turned resolutely to face him. She would not wait for him to ask the purpose of her visit. She must speak now, quickly, before her courage ebbed. "This morning you said you wanted to paint me."

An odd expression appeared in his eyes. "I did. You declined."

"Now I accept."

She was staring at the mantelpiece, as if she had never seen one like it. Seconds passed. At a continuing silence she turned her head. "Well?" She turned to look at him.

His thoughtful gaze was on her face. It lingered a long moment on eyes that were not quite steady, on lips that had once opened willingly beneath his. Then it descended to take in the little pulse beating too fast at the hollow of her throat, before descending, quite blatantly, to her shoulders and the rise and fall of her breasts beneath the soft pink fabric of the dress.

"You haven't forgotten how I'd paint you?" he asked at length.

She swallowed. "No."

"A street girl." He drew out the words, as if they gave him pleasure. "You do understand that, Cindy?"

"Yes." Her breath came shallowly.

The eyes that returned to her face had a look of mistrust. "There has to be a reason." One hand went out, to trail down her throat. "Some kind of sexual titillation?"

How dared he, she wondered.

She lifted her chin and looked him straight in the eyes. "Money," she pronounced.

A new expression came into his eyes. A deeper contempt than anything she had thus seen. Sickened, she turned away. But the hand on her throat came up once more to hold her chin and turned her to face him.

"Why?" Just one word. Very softly.

"Why not?" She shrugged. "I'm not living in the lap of luxury—as you must have noticed."

"Perhaps not. But you seem comfortable enough."

"Comfortable." She tossed the word at him flippantly. "A girl wants more than comfort, Jason. There are all sorts of things I'd like to have. Clothes . . . ." She cast around in her mind for material objects. "Pretty jewelry."

"And you'd prostitute yourself for that?" Still that watchful look. As if he didn't quite believe her.

He was getting to her. He did not know how much he was hurting her. Or perhaps he did. But for Jeremy's sake she had to rise above her own sensitivity.

"It is the oldest profession," she reminded him lightly.

81

"Could I have misjudged you so badly?" Thoughtfulness now, replacing contempt. "Perhaps I was a fool, Cindy, but I took you for sweet and innocent."

Over the lump in her throat she swallowed. "I must have seemed very boring."

"Boring?" A dangerous gleam in the dark eyes. "You were never that. It's the one accusation I can't level at you even now."

The lump was getting bigger. It was time to change the subject, before emotion could stand in the way of her decision.

"That's all rather by the by," she tossed at him saucily. "Do you want to paint me or don't you?"

"I'll tell you that when you've answered one question."

"Yes?" She waited, tensed, scarcely breathing.

"Why do you need the money?"

A small tongue went out to wet dry lips. "I thought I told you. I miss the luxuries of life."

"I keep wondering if there's something you've kept back."

His eyes were steady, perceptive. No mockery now. There was just thoughtfulness, questioning. Cindy forced herself to look away from him, for if she did not his expression could be her undoing. The temptation was there to confide in him, to tell him the truth, to lean on him for the moral and emotional support that she knew, instinctively, it was in him to give. But she could not do it. There flashed through her mind a picture of Beulah Mason. The woman's words were as clear today as they had been three years ago. "When Jason found out that you had never slept with a man before he felt honor bound to marry you." And then, "He will not stop seeing me."

Now again Cindy could have him. The sense of honor that had prompted his first proposal would be even stronger now when there was a child to consider. But much as she craved Jason's help and support, she could not accept them on those terms.

Tightly she said, "I haven't kept back a thing."

"Get undressed."

"Wh...what?" Her composure deserted her. She gaped at him.

"Get undressed." His tone was clipped and precise.

"Why?"

"You come to me with a business proposal. It's my right to see what I'm getting before I agree to terms."

"You...you know what I look like." The words emerged painfully.

"Do I?" His voice was drawling, seductive.

"You...you made love to me.... You saw me then." *Don't do this to me, Jason. Don't make it so damned hard.*

"I'm not sure I saw you properly even then. I saw a virgin. An innocent girl." His voice hardened. "And she wasn't innocent or a virgin after all."

83

She lifted her chin, green eyes meeting gray ones in open challenge. "In that case you'll find nothing changed."

She thought she saw the mobile lips tighten a fraction. But his tone was quite without expression when he said, "I need to satisfy myself on that point. You're secondhand goods now, Cindy Greerson. You slept with Andrew. You seduced me, thinking you'd get a father for your child. How many other men have you slept with? And how many of them have left their mark?"

There was only rage now as she lifted her hand to his face, only satisfaction in a stinging slap. "Go to hell, Jason!" she flung at him blindly.

"I've been there a long time," came the surprising answer. And then, as she turned from him and made for the gate, "You've decided against being painted?"

"Yes!" She was not thinking as she flung the word through the wind.

He reached her as she opened the gate, his hand closing over her shoulder. "So your pride is more important than the money?"

She stood quite still as the words made their impact. The sun burned down, but her body felt cold, as if a chill had passed through her, so that only her shoulder, where his fingers bit into the skin, tingled with heat.

Jeremy.... She had let temper get in the way of Jeremy's only chance.

Slowly, very slowly, she turned her head. Tears were trembling beneath her lids, but somehow she managed to keep them back.

"I'll get undressed," she said dully.

CHAPTER FIVE

THE CHILL was with her still as she followed him into the cottage to the room he had decided to use as his studio. She felt quite numb, nerveless, as if there was nothing that could make her laugh or cry. In a way this was good, she supposed, an anesthetizing effect that dulled the emotions so that it was easier to proceed with the degrading process she had set in motion.

In the walk from the gate back to the house and the studio not a word had passed between them. Now, in the big light-filled room he turned to her. "Get on with it."

Anger welled at the terseness of the order. Only the thought of Jeremy stopped her expressing it. "Turn around," she said.

A sardonic lift of one well-shaped eyebrow. "You know better than to ask me that."

"Please," she whispered, her lips feeling cold and drained of blood. "This isn't easy for me."

He uttered a mirthless laugh. "A good act, Cindy. Three years ago I'd have been convinced. But not now. We both know your modesty is nothing but coyness.

She stared at him a moment without speaking. Had he always been so cruel? So unfeeling? He was leaning back against a chest of drawers, one leg crossed negligently over the other. His hands were stuck in the waistband of his trousers. His whole posture spoke of strength and power and ruthlessness. There was also the maleness, the sheer virile maleness that had driven her crazy in the past. It was a quality she must disregard—if she could. Emotions must on no account be allowed any sort of rein. Jason had become her enemy. She must remember that and behave accordingly. For the present he had the upper hand. If she did not do what he asked he could easily decide not to paint her. Jeremy's only chance would vanish.

Her shoulders straightened. "All right, then," she said quietly, her fingers going to the buttons of her dress. Her eyes met his, quite deliberately, hoping to shame him into looking away. But his gaze did not waver.

Somehow she managed to order some direction into her nerveless fingers. There were six buttons; in a few seconds all had been opened. She paused a moment then, wondering if the man at the window would soften. But his face was without expression, the lines chiseled and angular like one of the sculptures she had seen in his Durban studio.

She slipped the dress from her shoulders, then directed her fingers to the opening of her bra. For a moment she hesitated, she *could not* take it off. And then she saw his eyes, his relentlessness. As she let the garment drop she was overcome with an urge to hide her breasts with her hands. Only a sheer effort of will kept her hands at her sides.

If she must stand before him like this, like some slave girl of old passing inspection before a prospective buyer, at least let it be with dignity. She tilted her head back just a fraction, so that her throat made a fluid line from skull to chest. Outwardly she was all pride and composure; inside she felt humiliated and cheapened.

The night when she had lain willingly in his arms seemed a long time ago. Then, too, her breasts had been exposed, not only to his eyes, but to his lips and his hands. That night had been beautiful. Now there was only degradation.

As their eyes met once more she was engulfed by a feeling that was stronger than anything she had ever known. Hatred! She hated Jason for what he was doing to her.

Dimly she knew that her emotions were not quite as simple as that; she sensed that hate and love could be closely interwoven. But this was not the moment for analysis. She knew only that he was making her suffer quite deliberately, and for that she could feel nothing but hate.

There was silence in the room. A silence so intense that Cindy felt she could actually touch it. There was tension, also. She had intended to wait for him to speak, but the silence coupled with his masterful and unmoving stance unnerved her.

"Well?" she asked, when she could not stand the strain a moment longer.

"Well," he countered lazily.

"Do I pass?"

The corners of his lips curved in a smile. It was a smile that did not reach his eyes. She could see a narrow expanse of teeth, the white glint against his tan making him look more dangerous than ever. A shiver rose inside her. Somehow she suppressed it.

And then he was coming toward her. She forced herself to stand very still. A long-fingered hand traced the lines of her body, from her throat down to the curve of her breasts and the line of her waist, and then farther, along gently rounded hips and thighs. Once these fingers had belonged to a lover, caressing, tantalizing, drawing forth a response she had not known she possessed. Now they were the fingers of an artist, examining a subject for line and shape and texture.

"You pass." His voice was dry, unemotional.

"When do we start?"

Could this conversation really be taking place, she wondered wildly. These words, flat and hateful, were a commercial exchange between two business partners. And all the time the fingers of the man were sending tingling shivers burning on her flesh where they touched it, and his breath, cool and clean, fanned the heat of her cheeks.

"Tomorrow. At ten. If the light is good."

"Fine." She took a step away from him. "There's one thing we haven't discussed."

His eyebrows lifted. He knew only too well what she meant, but he was making her spell it out.

She let him have it squarely. "Money."

"How much?"

Despite her resolve to be strong there was a dryness in her mouth. She swallowed hard. "A thousand rand."

Something came and went in his eyes. She had shocked him she thought, and felt a flicker of satisfaction.

His lips curled. "You set a high price."

Her fingers curled in her palms, her hands clenching to prevent them, even now, from covering her body. "No more than I'm worth," she informed him from beneath lowered lashes.

As she waited for his answer she was one mass of pain. The muscles of her stomach had knotted with tension, and her temples were aching. The figure she had named was high—very high. She knew that. But it was what she needed for Jeremy.

What would she do if Jason said no? If he bargained her down she would have to settle for a lesser amount. Hurt pride did not come into it. She would have to take what she could get and find some other way of raising the balance.

"Well?" she asked, when she could stand the suspense no longer.

There was an enigmatic light in the gray eyes that studied her. "It's a deal."

The relief of it! Until she expelled her breath with a tiny hissing sound she had not even known that she was holding it. The sheer relief! There would be degradation in the weeks to come, unhappiness and shame. But all that was part of the price she was willing to pay for the health of her child. For a moment she forgot that Jason was the enemy, that she must maintain the image of a brazen girl who was only out for what she could get. As she looked at him, wordlessly, she did not know that her eyes were luminous with unshed tears.

Perhaps he registered something of her emotion, for his own eyes narrowed. He seemed about to say something, then changed his mind. After another moment he said, "Get dressed." His tone was rough.

He was turning away from her when she found her voice. "Jason...?"

He spun around abruptly. "Yes?"

"You do understand that there will be nothing but painting?"

"And what the hell are you trying to tell me now?" he asked softly, dangerously.

Too late she realized that she should have kept this discussion for later, when she was dressed and not quite so vulnerable. Having begun, she had to go on.

"When I pose...I.... Well, it will be purely a business arrangement...." She cursed the nervousness that made her words emerge in a stammer and brought a flush to her cheeks.

"Meaning?" The expression in the chiseled face had never been more ominous. He recognized her embarrassment, she thought, and was glad of it. He knew only too well what she was getting at, but he wanted to hear her put it into words. He was sparing her nothing.

Not for the first time anger came to her rescue. Proudly she lifted her chin. "Meaning that you won't touch me."

Something flickered in his eyes. "So you think you set all the terms?"

Fear was a tangible quality. "Only those that concern me."

"Don't kid yourself, Cindy." His hands gripped her shoulders. He was standing just close enough to her so that she could feel the warmth of his body through his clothes.

"Let me go!" Her lips were so numb that it was hard to get the words out.

"When I'm ready to." His tone was hard and mocking.

She felt him draw her fractionally closer. The

clean male smell of him was so potent that it dizzied her senses. "Please, Jason...." she whispered.

"You're inviting me to make love to you."

Blindly she shook her head. "No!"

"Yes," he insisted. "You've been inviting it from the moment you came into this room."

"I don't want you to...." If he came any closer she would be lost. Her body, so long denied his touch, was crying out for his embrace.

"We both know what we want."

And then his mouth was on hers, crushing it mercilessly. One hand knotted in her hair, while the other moved over her back, molding itself to the shape of her waist and her hips and then down to her thighs, pressing the soft naked body easily against his. His touch, punishment though it was meant to be, was like manna after a long famine. There was no thought as she wound her arms around his waist and arched even closer against him.

She felt him stiffen. Then his mouth left hers and pulled at the hands that held him, dropping them abruptly to her sides. She stared up at him, painfully, uncomprehendingly, her eyes taking a few seconds to register his expression. So hard, so bleak....

"Tomorrow. Ten sharp."

Three words, clipped and precise. Without another look he turned on his heel and left her.

It was warm in the sun-filled room, yet Cindy felt very cold as she watched the door close behind him. It was a cold that seemed to penetrate to the very marrow of her bones. For what appeared a long time, but might have been no more than seconds, she stood motionless, unable to move a hand or a foot.

It came to her only gradually that she was standing in Jason's studio, and that she was totally naked. On the floor where she had dropped them were her clothes. A small pathetic heap.

Her fingers were shaking as she dressed, fumbling over the clasp of her bra, haphazard in the fastening of buttons. She had to get out of this house.

Opening the door of the studio she looked up and down the passage. Jason was nowhere in sight. His disappearance owed nothing to tact, Cindy knew. He would not think of being tactful to someone he did not respect and he had made his lack of respect perfectly clear. If he had left the cottage now it was purely because there was somewhere else he wanted to be.

She kept her eyes straight in front of her as she walked down the path to the rusty-hinged gate and then up the road toward Poinsettia. Her chin was high, her shoulders straight. Even in the depths of her despair she knew that she had to keep up appearances on the off chance that Jason might be watching.

She had intended going directly from the cottage to fetch Jeremy from Mrs. Langley. But she could not enter the rust-tiled kitchen of Graham's mother in her present state. Such were her feelings of fury and despair that she would not be able to hide them. Mrs. Langley would be puzzled and discuss her with Graham. Worse, Jeremy would be frightened. He had sensed her mood yesterday, when she had come trembling into the farmhouse after catching her first glimpse of Jason. Today, with her nerves heightened to breaking point, he would be even more affected.

Her son would not be hurt, she vowed grimly. Enough pain and suffering lay ahead of him in the months to come. He certainly did not need the additional stress of adult conflict. His parents' conflict.

His parents.... The words seemed ironic.

But for her own self, too, she had to go home first. If the last hour had left her feeling more enraged than she had ever been, it had also made her feel cheapened and dirtied. The knowledge that what she proposed to do was justified because Jeremy needed it, did nothing to lessen these feelings.

Reaching the driveway that led to the Poinsettia farmhouse, she ran the rest of the way—into her bedroom, to tear off her clothes with savage speed, then through to the bathroom. The water pouring out of the shower taps was strong and hot, a little too hot for comfort, but she did nothing to moderate it. There was some relief in feeling the water lashing her body, a symbolic cleansing away of the humiliation to which Jason had subjected it.

When she was dry and dressed—fresh clothes now, for she felt that she never wanted to see the halter-necked dress again—she left the farmhouse. It was time to fetch Jeremy.

She was at the crossroads, one of which led to the Langleys', when she glanced at her watch. Graham's mother would not mind if Jeremy was with her a while longer. In the absence of grandchildren of her own she seemed to enjoy the child's company, and for once Cindy felt an absolute need to be quite alone.

It was a good day for walking. Although it was hot as always on the tropical coastal belt, the wind that came from the sea was cooling. The sky was a metallic blue against the vivid colors of the land. On both sides of the road lay fruit farms. Cindy saw mangoes, velvet skinned and nearly ripe; peaches and plums, greengages and nectarines. Once she passed a pineapple farm, the pointed crowns of the fruit making a spiky geometric pattern on the ground. Banana palms grew wild at the roadside, and here and there stood a papaw tree, with the still-green fruit in clusters of tight balls.

A cart clattered along the rutted tracks of the road. As it passed her Cindy saw that it was piled high with articles of woven straw—broad-rimmed hats and baskets of all sizes. It was on its way to one of the holiday beaches, she knew, where the girls who guided the donkeys would set up their merchandise above the sands to take part in the daily tourist market.

The girls waved and called out as the donkeys ambled past. Cindy waved back, yet for once she could not smile. Normally she loved the sights and sounds of the countryside, the friendliness and the easy informality of the people. But today nothing seemed to penetrate the tight shell of her unhappiness.

As she passed the last of the farms the path narrowed beneath a tumble of roots and prickly seaflowers. Sand crunched underfoot and sifted in through open sandals as Cindy followed the path around the head of a high cliff. She had never walked this way with Jeremy—the going would be too hard for the little boy, and at the end of the road there would be nothing for him to do—but Cindy remembered coming here with John years before. Her brother had loved the high promontory with its wide ocean vista. At that time he had had dreams of going to sea, and it was a rare day when a few vessels could not be seen from this point. How uncomplicated life had been then. Or so it seemed to her now, looking back.

There had been a bench at the end of the path, placed there no doubt by someone who had loved the view as much as John did. Rounding the last bend Cindy saw that the bench was still in its place.

It was faded now, and a few planks were missing, nevertheless somehow it had withstood most of the ravages of wind and weather.

She sat down on the bench and stared out at the cobalt sea. The wind lifted her hair, tossing the auburn tendrils backward from her cheeks. A fishing trawler skimmed the waves, bobbing with the movement of the surf, and on the horizon, no bigger than toys from this distance, two ships were silhouetted. The young John would have sailed with them in fantasy while he regaled his sister with stories of the places he would one day visit.

Little had John known then that he would never be a sailor, but that he was destined to spend his life at a draftsman's drawing board instead. As for his sister, she, too, was a very different person now from the little girl who had knelt on the rough turf, making a chain of flowers. Was anything left of the girl who had delighted to run barefoot over the sand after the tide had retreated, who had enjoyed music and fun, and who had trusted people without fear of suspicion that she might end up getting hurt?

Tomorrow would be the first sitting, Jason had said. At ten o'clock. Would she have the strength to go down the road to his cottage and present herself in his studio? Would she be able to take off her clothes again and sit for hours while he sketched her? And would she be able to endure the final horror of seeing the finished portrait? Of knowing that her image would be hung on an exhibition wall in the guise of a street girl?

It should not matter that anyone who might recognize her as the model would believe that Jason held her in such low esteem; that he was prepared to paint her only in the most degrading of roles. All that mattered was that she would be paid one thousand rand, and that Jeremy would be able to have the operation that would give him a future.

Impatiently she shook herself. Ever since leaving the studio she had been unhappy at the humiliation she had suffered. In her despair she had overlooked the only thing that counted—the money for Jeremy's operation. Yesterday it had seemed so unlikely that she would be able to scrape up sufficient, that she had wondered at her temerity in telling the doctor that the operation would be performed. Today the money was assured. All she needed to earn it was time and patience and the ability to subdue her pride.

She could do it! She would! Her shoulders stiffened against the rough back of the bench as she thought of the days that lay ahead. She would take off her clothes, and she would sit on the dais in Jason's studio, and she would let him draw her. On the visual level she would not withhold herself from him. Not with so much at stake.

And yet there was another level of her being that must withdraw from the room and from Jason's presence. Mentally and emotionally she must try to absent herself from the studio, for if she failed in that he would haunt her for the rest of her life. It was a fact she could no longer deny to herself.

Three years ago she had fallen in love with Jason. Had loved him so much that she had slept with him and borne his child. But she was no longer the starry-eyed girl she had been then. She was a woman who had suffered and worked, who had brought up a delicate child and spent sleepless nights agonizing over his future. Yesterday, had she been asked if Jason still meant anything to her, her answer would have been simple. He was a memory, a memory who lived in the face of her child; who had brought her love and grief; who appeared sometimes in her dreams at night, but who featured little in the routine of her daily life.

In a few hours all had changed. Humiliation was not the only reality that must be faced and, for the time being, accepted. To herself Cindy had to admit that even after all this time Jason still had the power to stir her. The memory of the scene in the studio was vividly painful. There had been nothing but mockery in his embrace—mockery and contempt and a desire to demonstrate his mastery over her. Which made nonsense of the fact that her body had yearned to prolong it.

In some ways he was no longer the Jason she had once known. He had changed, just as she had changed. There were tiny lines around his eyes and mouth that she did not remember from before.

There was a deepened sternness and asceticism in the chiseled features. There was a desire to mock and wound that she had not suspected in him. Or was it just that she had never given him cause to let these qualities rise to the surface?

Watching the rise and toss of the waves, Cindy wondered what had wrought the changes. There was so much she did not know about the man she had once loved. If time had brought suffering to her own life, it might have brought its share to Jason's, also. Hard though it was to visualize. From the art reviews she read sometimes in the newspapers she had gathered that his career was as successful as ever. His portraits were even more in demand now than they had been, and commanded sums that to Cindy seemed like a fortune.

About his personal life she knew substantially less. There had been the odd picture in the social pages—Jason at the opening of an exhibition or at the first night of a new play. In these pictures he was never alone. Always by his side, clinging possessively to his arm, had been a beautiful woman— usually Beulah. The association between them was evidently as strong as ever.

The wind grew stronger. It tore at Cindy's hair and howled in her ears and threw drops of spray against her face. A fitting accompaniment to her own mood, she thought, as her tongue went out to lick the salt from her lips. But if there was fury in the wind there was healing, also. As she began to make her way back along the tangled path, she was glad that she had spent some time on the lonely cliff. Unhappiness still existed inside her. Perhaps it always would. Just as there would always be a longing for something that had been precious and special. Yet mixed with the unhappiness was a measure of acceptance. To some extent she had come to terms with herself and what had happened.

She would sit for Jason. At the same time she would try to detach herself emotionally from everything that he stood for in her life. With luck she would succeed. But if she did not, the adherent unhappiness would be an emotion she would cope with. And if that proved difficult, the sight of her child and the knowledge that he would soon be well would make it all worthwhile.

CINDY ROSE EARLY the next day. Ten o'clock, Jason had said, and his tone had indicated that he meant her to be on time. She had stipulated a high price and she had no doubt at all that he would set his own terms equally high. If she was to receive the money she had asked for she would have to be on time, so that Jason would have the benefit of the hours when the studio was at its lightest. She would have to take up the poses he wanted, even if they entailed stiffness or discomfort. And she would have to allow herself to be the victim of his contempt. If he meant to paint her as a street girl there would be much of that.

After a night in which her troubled mind had allowed her less sleep than she needed, Jeremy called from his room. One look at the small frail face reminded her of her priorities. Hugging the tiny body to her, she knew that there was no going back.

As she hurried through her chores she was glad that she had decided to make an early start. There were farmyard tasks that could not wait until the sitting was finished. If the chores were a necessity, they were therapy, too. There was so much to do that Cindy had little time to dwell on the ordeal that lay ahead.

When the chickens had been fed and the last of her seedlings watered, Cindy closed the kitchen door behind her. She held Jeremy's hand as they left Poinsettia behind them and started down the road. She kept her eyes straight ahead as they passed Jason's cottage. If he saw them she did not know it; she did not want to see him.

Graham's mother was waiting. "Will the sittings last long?" she wanted to know as she led the little boy inside.

Cindy was caught by something in her tone. "I...I'm not sure."

"Not that I mind, of course. Graham just wondered...."

So she had discussed it with Graham. And he hadn't approved. Did Graham have the right to disapprove, she wondered. Directly on the heels of

103

that thought came the acknowledgement that she should be glad of Graham's concern. It was good to know she had at least one friend. If only his disapproval did not smack of possessiveness. For with that would come complications, and Cindy felt she had enough of those to cope with already.

"I'll ask Mr. Peel," she said more crisply than she intended.

"It's not necessary." Brown eyes warmed in a smile. It was as if the woman sensed something of her tension, Cindy thought gratefully, and regretted the impatience that had crept into her tone. "I love Jeremy's company."

Returning to Poinsettia, Cindy glanced at her watch. Twenty minutes to ten. And still she had not decided what to wear. Not the dress she had worn yesterday. She would never wear that again! Riffling through her clothes it came to her that nothing in her wardrobe was suitable for the subject Jason had in mind. She did not know what was worn by women who lingered on street corners at night, hoping to lure customers with their charms. But she was not so naive as to imagine that any of her own clothes would fit the bill.

At length she teamed a trimly belted green skirt with a round-necked blouse of white chiffon that showed off the softness of her throat and shoulders before gathering at the tops of her arms in tiny tucks.

Twelve minutes left. Cindy dashed cold water

104

over a face that was hot and a little flushed after the hurried walk, and then looked at her hair. Normally she wore it in a simple style. For the kind of picture Jason contemplated something more alluring would be called for. Perhaps he imagined her with her hair drawn around to one side and a rose above her ear. She grimaced as she brushed her hair to hang soft and loose around her face. A few stray curls fell forward over her cheeks, and she pushed them impatiently backward.

The image in her mirror did not reflect her idea of a lady of the night, beautiful and seductive. But Jason would have his own ideas. Somehow she knew that he would not hesitate to make use of them.

Her heart was racing as she left the house and began to walk down the lane. Remoteness, she reminded herself, detachment. All Jason should see was a shell, and let him make of that what he wished. He must know nothing of the thoughts and emotions that gave the shell life. Only thus could she survive the ordeal that lay ahead of her. As she approached the cottage she lifted her chin and set her lips in a half smile. If Jason was watching out for her he would see only a young woman who was unconcerned and fancy-free, with nothing more on her mind than the money that could buy her the frivolous luxuries she desired. He would not know that even now, despite all her resolutions, her heart was beating so fast that it made a painful tattoo against her ribs.

A minute to go as she knocked on the door. He opened it almost immediately. For a long moment he stood looking down at her, taking in every detail of her appearance. Then he said, "Right on time."

She slanted him a glance from beneath her long lashes. "Did you expect otherwise?"

"Not for the kind of money you're asking." His eyes held a mocking gleam. "Come along, Cindy."

CHAPTER SIX

NOT EXACTLY A PROPITIOUS BEGINNING, Cindy thought as she followed Jason down the passage to the studio. And so different from the last time she had sat for him. Then there had been no commercial overtones to their relationship—only friendship and a reaching out of body and mind. And finally, on her side at least, a love that had known no limits.

Though the commercial aspect was the only one that existed now, Cindy could not help wondering if Jason, too, was remembering. He could not help but do so, she thought. The question was—did he wish in any way that things were different?

"Where's the boy?" he asked as he stepped aside to let her precede him into the studio.

The boy.... His name is Jeremy and he is your son. "I've made arrangements with a friend," she said. "She'll take care of him when I'm here."

"He didn't mind being taken out so early?"

So he *had* watched them. For some reason color flared briefly in her cheeks. "Not really." She smiled. "Jeremy is an easy child."

He took a step toward her, dark eyes staring down into hers. "You're quite certain he isn't mine?"

The breath seemed to stop in her lungs. Had he noticed some similarity after all? Some family resemblance of which she was not aware? Surely Jason would have had no chance to observe the expressions that came sometimes into Jeremy's eyes, and the amusement that curved his lips into a crooked smile. And even if he had, they were expressions he would not recognize as being his own unless he had watched himself smile or frown in a mirror.

He knew nothing, could know nothing. He was just taking a chance. "No," she said, as matter-of-factly as she was able. "I told you yesterday about Andrew."

A hand shot out to grip her wrist. "You could be lying."

She tried to pull away, but the grip was unrelenting. "Why would I do that?"

He shrugged. "Three years ago I gave up trying to understand why you behave the way you do."

So the rejection had hurt him more than she had imagined. She had thought he would be relieved to find the marriage was off, so that he could conti-

108

nue his association with Beulah without the burden of a wife's disapproval. Evidently, despite his relief, his pride had taken a battering.

A small tongue went nervously to lips that were suddenly dry. "He is Andrew's son."

"How can you be sure?" His voice was very hard.

"It's a biological fact," she responded as flippantly as she could.

The grip on her hand tightened so that she winced. "Don't try your smart talk on me, Cindy. You slept with Andrew, you slept with me."

"Only one at a time." It was becoming harder and harder to speak.

"How many others did you sleep with?" he went on, ignoring her words.

The chilling tones changed the pain in her chest to a flaming anger. Jason had no right to talk to her like this. Whatever had happened between them he had no right to humiliate her at every turn.

"That's my business," she threw at him.

The lean face tightened so that the skin was stretched tautly over high cheekbones and a long jaw. "You little tart."

"Of course." A reckless laugh. "That's why I should make such a good model."

"Another minute and you'll be raising your price." She had not known he could be quite so hard, so eager to salt the wounds.

"I might do just that." Her voice was very low

now, as she held back a sudden rush of tears. There was just so much she could take, and she had the distinct feeling that she was reaching the limits of her control. "Shall we begin? I don't suppose these are the right clothes."

"An understatement. But then you knew that when you planned this getup. Outward innocence mixed with just the right blend of seductiveness. I have to hand it to you, my dear, you are an expert at the game."

She stared at him. The outfit was unsuitable, as she'd known it would be when she'd contemplated the lack of sophisticated garments her wardrobe contained. But she had not realized that he would take her choice as deliberate.

"Perhaps you'd like me to go back and change into my come-hither dress." Such was her anger at the moment that as she threw the question at him she almost forgot Jeremy and the need that had made her offer to sit for Jason in the first place; forgot the paucity of her wardrobe and the fact that if he took up her bluff she would be in a dilemma.

"That won't be necessary," he said easily, tossing her a flame-colored garment she had not noticed until now. "Put that on."

She hesitated. "If I don't?"

An eyebrow lifted sardonically. "Then I'll draw you nude. It makes little difference to me."

She wondered if he would watch her change as he had done yesterday. But he gestured to a curtained alcove, and as she walked toward it he turned to his drawing board.

The dress fitted as if made for her. There was a mirror behind the curtain. Cindy looked at herself, hating what she saw, yet marveling how a piece of fabric could so drastically change her appearance.

Naked or dressed, he had said either way made little difference. He had been right about that. She looked as if she had been poured into the dress—as if the scarlet stuff was a molten liquid that had taken solid substance as it fitted around her. The fabric was sheer, so transparent that it left nothing to the imagination. It clung to her body, molding itself to each line and curve, giving her a seductive voluptuousness she had not known she possessed. The dress was a modest floor-length, but up each side ran a slit that bared her legs to the tops of her thighs. The sleeves were long, also, fitting trimly around slender wrists, but the bodice was slashed to a plunging V that revealed the curve of her breasts and the top of her midriff.

Looking at herself in the mirror, Cindy knew it was the most outrageous garment she had ever worn. So artfully had the dress been designed that it gave her a more sensual appearance than she could ever have achieved unclothed.

"Cindy?" Jason called.

She put her head around the curtain. "You can't really expect me to wear this."

"It doesn't fit?" he drawled.

"It *fits*. But it's . . . it's unsuitable."

"The modesty game again."

While the mockery in Jason's voice geared her for another verbal battle, the laziness of the drawl left her unprepared for the speed with which he moved. One moment he was at the drawing board. The next, giving her no time to put up her defenses, he was at the curtain and pulling it aside.

He said nothing as he studied her, but she saw his eyes move slowly, insolently, over her hips and waist, upward to her breasts, and then up again, moving to her throat and her face, lingering on cheeks that were the color of the dress and eyes that were wide and green and stormy.

"Very suitable indeed," he said softly.

"No!" Pain was a hard dry lump in her throat.

He took a step closer. Her heart was thudding, and she knew that in the tiny hollow at the base of her throat the racing pulse made her vulnerable. She took a step backward and found herself backed against the wall.

She heard him laugh—the laugh that did disturbing things to her senses. Then he reached out a hand and put it very softly against one thigh. Slowly, tantalizingly, the hand moved, the long fingers brushing over the outward curve of the thigh to the hip and up to the waist. She wanted to push the hand away. But she could not move. By now it was an effort just to breathe. The long fingers teased and explored, the touch so light that it was a tantalizing torture to frenzied senses. Higher it went, over a midriff that was bare, moving on the skin just above the navel, then higher still to the swell of breast on each side, tracing a mark of fire over skin that was so sensitive that it seemed to cry out a wordless appeal. To stop or to go on? Cindy could not have said at this moment what that cry was, but whatever its meaning Jason paid it no heed. His fingers were merciless, unrelenting. They probed farther, sliding beneath the fabric of the dress to where the nipples strained, and then out again, up to the hollow of her throat and the telltale pulse.

"You are wrong," he said softly.

"Wrong?" The word came out in a rasping whisper.

She saw his lips curve. He had registered her emotions—the embarrassment, the vulnerability, the unreasoning desire of a body turned traitor to her mind—and was satisfied.

"The dress is more than suitable. Come along, Cindy."

"I can't." The words emerged painfully.

He looked at her. "You've changed your mind?"

She nodded blindly. "I can't go on with this."

A shrug. "Just as you like."

She was moving back to the alcove when his next words stopped her. "So you'll put scruples before money after all."

She stopped in midstep. Money.... The word

113

registered like a brand on a dulled mind. Jeremy and his operation. There could be only one answer. Jeremy was her child—helpless, trusting, dependant on her not only for the normal maternal comforts but for his health, perhaps his life.

"I'll sit for you," she said dully.

The dark eyes were watching her. "Why?"

The question brought a small flare of returning spirit. "Does it matter? Perhaps because the fripperies I can buy with a thousand rand mean a lot to me. Let's just get on with it, Jason."

The dais was ready. A very different dais from the one she had posed on three years earlier. Now there was a cushion covered in amber-colored silk, and beneath it a matching sheet. The chaise loungue of a courtesan. Jason had certainly wasted no time since yesterday. He must have driven into the nearest town and made a few purchases, Cindy thought.

She lifted her head as she walked past him and eased herself down. Perhaps the tilt of the chin was no more than a hollow gesture. He might well recognize it for defiance, and be amused at its futility. That did not seem to matter. What was important was that despite her seeming subservience and greed, Jason should know that she was still a creature of spirit and will who would dance to his puppeteer's strings only for as long as it suited her to do so.

He stood quite still, studying her posture. When his eyes met hers she was ready for him, holding

114

his gaze with a look that was steady and unafraid. Again she saw something flicker in his eyes. Hard to define what it was. In any other man she might have taken the look for admiration. But Jason was not any other man, and he did not admire her. His contempt was clearer every moment. Despite herself the blood leaped briefly in her veins.

"Not bad. But not quite right." He was matter-of-fact now. Whatever the expression had implied, if she had not in fact imagined it, now it was gone.

"Bend your left leg a little," he told her. "No, Cindy, not like that. You're not a child." He came to the dais and as he positioned her leg, moving her ankle, pulling at her knee and thigh, she drew on every resource she possessed to prevent the trembling that threatened to engulf her.

He stood back and tilted his head thoughtfully to one side. "Better. Much better. Remember what you're meant to be, Cindy. A lady of the night makes her postures seductive."

As he walked to the drawing board she wondered if he realized the irony of his words. If she was indeed what he thought her, then she would need no guidance. But she did not speak. To do so would be to invite further verbal sparring, and she was not ready for it. The turmoil within her was more than she could safely cope with for the moment.

Sitting for Jason would be even worse than she had imagined. She knew that now. She grimaced as she remembered the injunctions she had given herself—detachment, aloofness, emotions under strict rein. Alone on the cliff with the surf thundering below her, it had seemed possible to keep herself apart from him in every sense save the visual. Easy enough to theorize when she surveyed the situation from a distance. Unbelievably difficult in practice, when every nerve and fiber of her being responded to his touch, his nearness and the sheer sexual impact of the man.

One thing to reason with the mind, quite another to order her body. The rational part of her was outraged at the callousness of Jason's behavior. The sensual part of her seemed not to care, wanting only to be close to him, part of him even....

How long would it take for him to finish the portrait? Five sittings? Six? Even one was more than she could manage. The thought of the days that lay ahead was a nightmare.

Jeremy! She had to hold on to the thought of her child. Only that way lay sanity. Jason was the man who could stir her blood and dizzy her senses and drive her to madness. But Jeremy was the child she had borne of a moment when she had been truly in love. He was the focal point of her life, the being she loved more than anyone and anything in the world. Her present ordeal, endless though it now seemed, could in fact only be transitory. Jeremy's resulting benefits would stand him in good stead for the rest of his life. This was all that mattered.

Opposite her Jason was working. The long fingers moved over the page, swiftly, surely, never fumbling. The fingers of the artist bringing life and personality to a sheet. The fingers of a lover, who had once stirred her to ecstasy and fulfillment. The fingers of a man who was an expert where women's responses were concerned.

Time passed—minutes, hours. Jason did not talk as he worked. Now and then he looked up and studied her. When he did so it was impersonally, seeking only to satisfy himself on a detail. Gone now were the new qualities of mockery and contempt that, after only two days, she had come to hate. Gone was the momentary flicker she had seen in his eyes when she had made her gesture of defiance as she went to the silk-draped dais. She had been crazy to think even for a moment that the expression could have denoted admiration. Whatever it had been, it had not been that. Gone was the deliberate seductiveness with which he explored her body and roused her senses. The man who sat at the drawing board was now solely an artist who could suggest an emotion or a quality in the subtle nuances of a few lines.

And then at last the sitting was over. Dressed in her own clothes once more Cindy came out of the alcove to find Jason covering the drawing board. If he heard her he gave no sign. She paused a moment, wondering whether to walk out of the room without saying goodbye, or whether to say a few words; then decided on the latter course. The next sitting might be easier if some rapport was established between them. Besides, she was curious....

"How did it go?"

He looked up with a glimmer of a smile. "Fine. You're a good model."

Did he refer to her new role? Cindy felt the need to defend herself. "You said that three years ago."

"I say it again."

Now was the time to call a halt to the conversation, before things were said that she would later regret. Yet some streak of devilment drove her further. "You said once that you paint what you see."

"I still do." The smile had become mocking.

His meaning could not be clearer. And still she had to go on. "How do you reconcile the innocent girl you once painted with the tart you see now?"

The look he gave her was long and level. For no reason at all she felt a weakness in her legs, but she forced herself not to show it. "That, my dear Cindy, is something I will have great pleasure in discovering. One thing is clear." He paused, and she saw an enigmatic expression in the narrowed gray eyes. "The girl I painted has two faces—and one of them is false."

Not hard to know what he meant. More than ever he was convinced that the Cindy he had known three years earlier was a schemer. In a way she had only herself to blame. It was the story she had given him, and he had no reason to disbelieve her. It made no sense then that there was a part of her that wished very much that he could see the truth behind the deception.

She swallowed. "May I see what you've done?"

"No."

"Jason...."

The mockery left his eyes, just as the smile had done moments earlier. Now his expression was cold, the long jaw stern and rigid. "Let's get one thing straight. You are only the model. I'm paying you a lot for these sittings. A darn sight more than anyone else would pay."

"Why did you agree?" she flashed at him, reckless of the consquences.

"Because it suited me," he countered smoothly. "But the portrait is mine—to do with whatever I like. And there's no way you'll see it unless I choose to show it to you."

She left the cottage without another word, walking quickly down the path and through the gate. Unlike the previous day she did not go first to Poinsettia. Not that the desire was not there. More than anything she longed for the cleansing of a shower and the healing quality of a walk on the windy cliff top. But these were luxuries she would not allow herself. For one thing, Jason could be watching where she went, and she did not want him to have the satisfaction of knowing how much the last few hours had disturbed her. For another, today the pattern for their working relationship had been set.

A business arrangement, purely that. Cindy was rendering a service for which Jason would pay her. That, in cold essence, was what today and the days to come were all about. To Jason, quite clearly, this was where the matter ended. If it meant something more to Cindy in terms of senses and emotions and memories, abstract qualities that she could neither change nor influence, then Jason was to remain ignorant of the fact.

She could only hope that the time would come when she herself would look upon the sittings only in terms of financial reward.

Arriving at the Langley farm, Cindy saw that a truck was parked outside the house. Graham must be home. Despite her resolve to be strong she could not prevent a feeling of apprehension. She had not seen Graham since agreeing to sit for Jason, but he knew of the arrangement from his mother. Though the young vet had no claim to her, she wondered what he would say.

The truck was the one he used for transporting sick animals. Through the open bars Cindy saw the flanks of a horse. As she came near, she heard voices on the far side of the vehicle—a low male tone and then a child's delighted laugh. Two heads turned as she approached.

"Horsey, momma. Horsey...." Jeremy's small face shone with excitement.

"I see it, darling. Hello, Graham."

"Hi." He was grinning, the lopsided boyish grin that was one of his most endearing qualities. Cindy wondered if it was only her heightened awareness that perceived the look of restraint in his eyes.

It was surprisingly hard to smile back at him. So fresh in her mind were the events of the past hours that normal human communication seemed a feat beyond her reach. She was surprised that she could force a teasing lightness into her tone as she touched on what was a well-worn private joke between them. "Converting my son to the joys of veterinary practice?"

"I never give up trying." For a moment Cindy had the feeling that he was talking of something quite different. Before she had a chance to think up a light rejoinder, Graham said, "He loves looking at my animals, and I enjoy showing them to him. Cindy—I believe you're posing for the fellow in the cottage."

It should not have been necessary for her chin to lift just fractionally to a defensive tilt. "Yes."

And then, as if some amplification was needed, "He...he's pretty well-known in artistic circles all over the country."

Brown eyes assessed her intently. "You did know him from before...?"

There was no stopping the two spots of color that stained her cheeks. "I told you...we...we'd met...."

121

"Cindy—"

"Graham, please," she interrupted him quickly, her hand going instinctively to a pounding temple. "I have to get back. Can we talk about this another time?"

"Of course." His tone was surprisingly cool. "Just one question—have you sat for Mr. Peel before."

She hesitated. "Does it matter?"

Brown eyes held hers steadily. "Yes."

It's none of your business, she longed to say. *I've had more than I can take for one day. Don't you start on me, also.*

Before she could speak Graham said, "Everything about you matters to me. I think you know that." And when she still stared at him, "That's why I'd like to know."

Now was not the time to deal with the implications contained in his words. "I understand," Cindy said quietly. "I sat for Jason Peel once...long ago.... And now...this is a business arrangement. You might as well know that."

"He's paying you, then?"

"Yes."

"And you're putting the money toward Jeremy's operation." Graham eyed her with steady comprehension. "I should feel better knowing that, shouldn't I? Isn't it strange that I don't?"

"Jeremy." Cindy bent to the child who was absorbed in the ailing horse, quite oblivious of an adult conversation that he would in any event not have been able to understand. "We have to start going, poppet."

"In a moment." A hand took her wrist, almost in the same spot where Jason had seized it earlier. "Did Jason Peel know you were living here? Is that why he came?"

The idea had occurred to her, but she had decided to reject it. What remained of her peace of mind depended on it. For if Jason had known where to find her then he would have come here deliberately—sought her out purely for the purpose of humiliating her.

She shook her head, her lips curving in a gamin smile. "I'd be flattering myself if I thought that."

"Perhaps you don't realize quite how lovely you are."

Green eyes danced in a deepening smile. "You do wonders for my morale, Graham. But it's really not the way you imagine. Jason—Mr. Peel needs a model. I happened to be conveniently available."

A wide jaw took on an unaccustomed rigidity. The familiarity reflected in the inadvertent use of the first name had not escaped Graham. "The fellow's been here only two days. He must be a fast worker."

It was becoming more and more difficult for Cindy to maintain her air of amused and relaxed composure. In a low voice she said, "It's a situation that suits us both. He needs a model. I need the money. Graham, my head is splitting. Please don't think me rude, but I'll just go inside and tell your mother that I've come for Jeremy and then we'll be on our way."

Graham insisted on giving them a lift back to Poinsettia, and Cindy was too tired to decline. The morning hours had drained her—first the ordeal in Jason's cottage and then the talk with Graham. She was very quiet on the short drive back from the Langley farm. Graham was quiet, too, as if he was preoccupied with his own thoughts, and she was grateful that she had no need to make further conversation. Only Jeremy's chatter filled the silence; the little boy babbled in his own brand of baby talk about the cookies he had helped Mrs. Langley bake and the sick horse in the back of the truck.

There was a flicker of movement as the truck passed Jason's cottage. Without turning her head, Cindy caught sight of a tall lean figure striding through the tangled garden. Had Jason seen her sitting in the truck? He could hardly have missed her.

Let him know that there were other men in her life, she thought with a tired flicker of satisfaction. As it was, his opinion of her morals could not be lower. But if he had any illusions that he was of importance to her, then the sooner these were dispelled the better. For if Jason were to guess that he still had the power to disturb her, his behavior would become even more intolerable than it was already.

Graham did not linger long at Poinsettia, and Cindy was glad. Despite his excitement Jeremy looked pale and tired, and she was keen to put him down for his nap. There were still the afternoon chores to see to. Tomorrow would be another long day, and she wanted to do as much as she could before dark.

Cindy was very tired by the time she went to bed at last, exhausted in body and mind. In a way it was an exhaustion she welcomed. There would be no brooding tonight at the open window of her room with the thunder of the sea and the headiness of tropical shrubs adding an unbearable poignancy to emotions already heightened beyond endurable limits. There would be only sleep, mindless and hopefully dreamless. Only for a few minutes did Jason manage to intrude into her thoughts. She was in the half-world between waking and sleeping when a tall figure with a lean and brooding face appeared for a few moments to hover before closed and heavy lids. And then the figure vanished as she sank, mercifully, into sleep.

CHAPTER SEVEN

THE DAYS began to take on a pattern. Jason wanted sittings only every second day, he told Cindy. On those days she rose early, washed her hair and brushed it as she had done the first time, with a few tendrils escaping to curl around her face. She hurried through the morning chores, took Jeremy to Mrs. Langley, and then it was back to Poinsettia for a shower and a change of clothes. She did not wear the skirt and blouse she had worn the first time. There was no need for the outfit, for at the cottage was the flame-colored dress that she was beginning to loathe.

The sittings stretched for long hours. Often Cindy grew stiff and tired, but Jason appeared neither sympathetic nor concerned, and she never complained. She would be getting a great deal of money for what she was doing, and any tediousness was part of that price. There were times when she grew restless—for Jason did not talk to her while he worked—and there were times when her head ached, but she never regretted her decision to pose for him. Constant in her mind was the knowledge that what she did would benefit her child.

Constant, also, was her awareness of Jason, an awareness that did not lessen with time. She would watch him as he worked and marvel anew at the changes in him. Perhaps the sternness, the asceticism, the arrogance, were qualities that had always been a part of his nature, but if so she had not noticed them. The man she had known three years earlier had had more lightness in him, more laughter. The bleakness she now saw so often in his eyes had not been there then. Nor the flatness of the voice. These things were new, just as the lines around his eyes, which she had noticed the day he had visited her at Poinsettia, were new.

She thought sometimes that what had once happened in a sunny house high on the hills of Durban might have taken place in another world, between two other people. Only one thing linked the past to the present, the Jason and Cindy of three years ago to the hostile strangers who worked together now. Jeremy, a child born of a flame that had sparked between them, creating a mutual need and desire; a child who required help beyond the loving care required by other children.

The link was one of which Jason would remain forever ignorant.

As she watched the long fingers moving over the drawing board, Cindy wondered, also, at the emotions that Jason had wrought in her. Once there had been love. An all-consuming love that had consumed every nerve and fiber of her being to the extent that she had been prepared to forget principles that until then she had held dear. Now there was hatred. Surely the emotion she felt had to be hatred. What else was possible toward a man who treated her with such open contempt, taking pleasure in humiliating her and satisfaction in seeing her embarrassed? Hatred could be the only thing she felt for him.

And yet in the midst of her reasoning there crept the desire to reach out from the dais to touch him; the longing to thread her fingers through the dark hair at the point where it lay thick and glossy above the edge of his collar; the longing to touch his cheeks and trace a path along his nose and around his mouth to the strong line of his jaw; the longing to slide a hand into his shirt and put her palm flat against the muscled chest. And the longing, crazier and more irrational than all the others, to feel his arms around her body and his legs hard against hers and his mouth on her lips.

It was a longing that sent the blood racing faster through her veins. It was a longing that she tried to suppress with all the willpower at her command. But in vain, so it seemed. Just as she was powerless to suppress the memories of a time when she had been more crazily in love than she had ever dreamed possible, so she could not shake off the longings that gripped her now.

So much for all the resolutions she had made on a lonely cliff top, she thought wryly. She had failed to take into account the potency of Jason's attractiveness, the sheer sensual impact of his maleness and the responses it provoked in her.

Once she had loved him, and now she hated him. Two separate facts clear and distinct. If only she could explain why the emotions seemed to overlap and merge so that when she thought she most hated him, those were the times when she most wanted him.

A wiser person than Cindy had said long ago that the line between hate and love was little more than the breadth of a hair, so that the two emotions often went hand in hand. When she had read the statement in a book she had dismissed it as the musings of a poet. For the first time she was forced to acknowledge that the poet might have written the truth.

She was so acutely aware of Jason that she wondered sometimes, a little wildly, if he could be unconscious of the tension that seemed to spark and tingle in the atmosphere between them, and yet the remoteness in his face indicated that the only thing on his mind was the picture taking shape before him.

He spoke to her only when he wanted her to change her posture—the position of a hand or the slope of a leg or the slant of her head. Sometimes she did not take up quite the position he wanted, and then he would come to her and rearrange her limbs with his hands. There was nothing personal in his touch at these times, Cindy knew; just the touch of an artist who was dissatisfied with a line or an angle. Yet when the long fingers rested on her skin she could no more still the wild leaping in her nerve stream than she could have stopped the breath in her lungs. At times like these she had to exercise every ounce of control she possessed, forcing an outward composure that was as detached as his own.

"How many more sittings?" she asked him once.

He looked up, "As many as it takes."

"I know...." She was oddly breathless. "But how many will that be?"

The remoteness left his eyes to be replaced by an expression of malicious amusement. "Why, Cindy? Are you already regretting our arrangement?"

As always his arrogance provoked her anger. "I didn't say that," she flashed.

"Perhaps you'd like the money without finishing your side of the bargain," he suggested lazily.

"I didn't say that, either. I asked you a simple question, Jason. How long?"

"I gave you the answer." The bleakness was back in his eyes. "As long as it takes."

And with that she had had to be satisfied. She

could only hope that the sittings would end soon. The longer she had to be in Jason's company, the more likely it was that she would yearn for him long after he had gone back to Durban. Already she knew that her chances of being happy with another man were dwindling. As much as she liked Graham, he was an insubstantial shadow of a man when she compared him with Jason. Useless to tell herself that Graham was kind and considerate and possessed of all the qualities that Jason would never have. In terms of emotional impact Graham could not compete with the man who had entered her life three years ago. Something told her no other man would compete with him ever.

THERE WAS A MORNING when the sky was heavy and gray. As Cindy took Jeremy to Mrs. Langley she glanced anxiously at the little boy. If only the rain kept off until they reached the Langley farm.

Briefly she had toyed with the idea of going to the cottage and telling Jason that she could not come. Then she dispensed with it. At their last session Jason had been even curter and more distant than usual. Their arrangement was clear. He was expecting her and would only treat any request that they postpone the sitting with contempt.

It had grown cold and the first drops were falling when she reached Jason's cottage. She shivered as she knocked at the door, glad that Jeremy was warm and dry with Mrs. Langley. No need to hurry back,

131

Graham's mother had said. If there was a storm she would look after the little boy until it stopped.

When Jason did not come to the door Cindy knocked again. Still no response. She was getting wet standing outside waiting for him. She turned the knob and found it open.

Jason was not in sight as she walked down the passage to the studio. Perhaps he was in the garden and had not heard her. In her hurry to beat the storm she had not gone first to Poinsettia and was earlier than usual. Not that it mattered. The red dress was on the hook behind the studio door. She could change into it, and be ready for him when he came.

She had slipped on the dress and was about to pull up the zipper when he entered the room. She stopped in midmovement, the zipper still open as her hands dropped to her sides. As she had suspected he had been outside, for his hair lay in damp strands across his forehead. He was wearing well-cut fawn trousers and a matching sweater of a thin fabric that clung to his chest, revealing the breadth of the shoulders and the muscles that rippled as he moved. These were not the clothes he normally kept for work in the studio.

More than anything else, she was caught by his expression. A look of surprise was in his eyes, a momentary look only. The gleam that replaced it had an enigmatic quality that she could not define, yet which sent her heart lurching uncomfortably against her ribs.

"You *were* expecting me?" she asked, and wished that she did not sound quite so shaky. "It *is* Friday."

"It's also overcast and beginning to rain."

She looked at him for a moment without answering. His face was wet, also, a burnished sheen against the tan. Perhaps because the spartan features had never looked more attractive, Cindy's comprehension was dulled.

"You were thinking of Jeremy," she said softly.

His jaw took on a hard line. "No," he said curtly. "I pay you well. Your baby-sitting arrangements are your own."

She looked at him through eyes that were green and pained, wondering why he sought to hurt her at every turn. "Then I don't understand...."

"The light." He gestured impatiently. "Didn't it occur to you that the studio would be dark?"

Perhaps she should have thought of it, but she hadn't. She recalled how she had hurried Jeremy through breakfast and the subsequent walk to the Langley farm. They would have to walk back later, also, when the storm had stilled. Jason could so easily have saved her all this unnecessary trouble.

Anger welled swiftly inside her. "You're a bastard, Jason Peel. You knew I'd come. If you didn't care to spare me you could at least have spared my child."

She turned, quickly, so that he would not see the tears that had sprung treacherously to her lashes. It was as if he would never grow tired of punishing her for the wrong he imagined she had done him. She forgot that the zipper of the dress was open. She wanted only to change back into her own clothes and to get out of the cottage as quickly as possible.

"Where are you going?" The voice behind her was very soft.

She did not turn. "Home."

"In the rain?"

"I won't melt," she said stiffly.

A pair of hands planted themselves on the bare skin beneath the parted zipper, the palms flat against her back so that she could feel every finger. The movement was unexpected, without warning, so that she was unable to control the tremor that shivered through her.

"I have to go." The words tumbled out on a shaken breath.

The hands moved, sliding farther beneath the dress, encircling her waist, spreading over the flatness of her stomach. "You're not going anywhere."

He was so close to her now that it was hard to think coherently. She could feel his chest against her back, and his thighs taut and muscled against her hips. When he spoke his lips moved in her hair. She must think! Now, when her senses were in danger of being swamped, she had to keep her wits about her.

"I have to go!" It was a wild cry, more vehement than the words justified.

"Why?" The merest whisper.

Let me go! Don't you know what you're doing to me? The torment you're putting me through? You do know, and it gives you pleasure. "Th...things I have to d-do," she managed.

He laughed, a sound that was low and seductive and infinitely unnerving. "Liar. You've done your chores and the child is at the baby-sitter."

"Yes, but—"

"But you're a coward," he finished for her. "You know that you want this, but you're frightened." His voice hardened a fraction. "In the circumstances I'm not sure why you should be."

He was thinking of the fictitious Andrew, of Graham—of himself. Even through the frenzy of her emotions it came to Cindy that she must tread warily. Too much reticence would be treated first with contempt, then with suspicion. And suspicion would lead to the truth—which must not happen.

Difficult as her act had been until now, it had become more difficult. Jason thought her worldly and a little jaded, with more than a few affairs to her credit. How would he reconcile this concept with the responses of a girl who was almost as innocent now as she had been at eighteen; a girl who ached for his lovemaking and was frightened at the same time?

There was only one way. "I'm not frightened."

Amazingly her voice came out strong and firm.

"No?" The soft mockery she hated.

"No. Just repelled." She threw it at him, as coolly and as matter-of-factly as she could.

She felt him stiffen against her, the hardness of his body rigid and tight. Then he said, "I wonder then how you explain the ease with which you fell into my bed three years ago?"

She tried to pull away from him, but the hands that held her gave no inch. "I've explained that. I...I needed a father for my child."

"Not good enough. It doesn't explain the passion of your lovemaking." The lips were back in her hair. "And you *were* passionate, Cindy. I can't believe that was all an act."

The situation was slipping out of her control. A little desperately she protested, "Perhaps it wasn't.... But I'm a different person now. Different wants, different...."

She stopped, the words stilled in her throat as the hands on the stomach moved upward, sliding over her breasts, cupping them easily. She could no more stop the frenzied rate of her heartbeat than she could stop her nipples from swelling and hardening beneath his hands.

"Your body speaks the truth where your words don't." Still the mockery was in his voice, but huskiness, also. He was so close to her now that the dampness of his shirt was a sensation of its own against her back. The longing within her was so intense that she could find no words to speak, and the taut hardness of his body revealed that he wanted her as much as she wanted him.

As his hands turned her, moving her in the circle of his arms until she was facing him, she made one last effort. "You don't even care for me."

He took so long to answer that she lifted her head to look at him. His eyes were narrowed, studying her with an intensity that scared her. It was as if a veil had been lifted from his vision, so that he was seeing something he had not seen before.

But when he spoke his tone was chilling as ever. "Caring has nothing to do with it, does it, Cindy? You are the one person who knows that."

Fright had made her careless. In asking the question she had slipped, just a little. "I do know it. Jason, I had a reason for sleeping with you then. I've no reason now."

"But you do. The best reason of all." A finger trailed from her waist up around the contours of her breasts, and then over the little hollow of her throat to her face. "You want me to make love to you. And if you deny that you're kidding yourself." And before she could answer he continued, "Don't talk about caring. We both know that doesn't come into it."

Even if she had been able to think of an adequate response the pain that came with his words would have stopped her from uttering it. For Jason caring did not exist. For her it did. Always would. The revelation—so soon after she'd told herself that she hated him—was frightening.

"We do know that, don't we?" His voice was insistent, tearing at the veneer of the image she had so carefully presented to him and to herself.

"Yes." She forced herself to meet his eyes. "We've always known it."

His gaze held hers a moment longer. There was a hardness in it more intense than anything she had seen there before. The gaze lingered over her face, then descended to her body, ruthlessly, deliberately, as if he wanted to hurt her in any way he could think of.

As his eyes came up again he pulled her roughly toward him. "You little tart," he ground out. "You beautiful, desirable little tart."

There was no pulling away from him as his mouth came down on hers with a savagery that was unlike anything she had ever known. For a few moments she resisted him, keeping her lips firmly closed as she reeled at the outrage of his punishment. His tongue was pushing at her lips, forcing them apart, but even before he achieved his object she found herself complying with a willingness that owed nothing to reason but was born solely from a frenzied response to the flame surging through her body. Tongue met tongue and teeth met teeth, and then he was nibbling at the soft sweetness of her mouth.

There was no thought as she wrapped her arms

around his waist and pressed her hips against his. She felt the involuntary shudder that ran through him, and then his hands were at the top of her dress, pushing it from her shoulders. She had to step a little away from him to let the garment fall to the floor, and then she was in his embrace once more.

His hands were on her back again, sliding down to her hips, molding her to him. New torrents of desire cascaded through her, igniting fires that defied reason and logic. As she arched willingly toward him there was only the need to be closer to him, and closer....

His hands moved over her, exploring, tantalizing, setting atingle every inch that he touched. His lips were in her hair, on her throat, her eyes, then moved downward to the hollow between her breasts.

And then he was lifting her, cradling her in his arms as easily as if she had been a doll. As he carried her through the door of the studio she knew he was taking her to his bedroom. She did not mind, did not care. She only gloried in the strength of the arms that held her, and nuzzled her face against the damp expanse of his chest.

He kicked open the door of his room and put her on the bed. For a long moment he looked down at her. No word passed between them as gray eyes and green eyes met and held. She saw a new expression, no mockery this time, nor bitterness. It was an expression she could not define. A kind of pain, perhaps, she thought, searching in vain for a more suitable word.

It came to her only later that pain was the one thing it could not have been.

She lay very still and saw the expression in his eyes deepen. "My God, you are beautiful!" She heard the huskiness in his tone, and then he was kneeling on the bed next to her. His fingers reached for her face. There was no passion now, no punishing savageness. Only a tenderness that was more agonizing than anything that had gone before. His fingers trailed a path around her temples, pushing aside the tendrils of hair that lay across her forehead and over her ears: trailed around her nose and mouth, down her throat, and then down toward her breasts, first around one nipple and then the other. The same path his lips had taken.

Inside Cindy was an ache such as she had never felt before. Not even at the height of her ecstasy three years earlier had she felt quite like this. Reaching to the head on her breast she locked her hands around his neck, burying her fingers in the thick rain-dampened hair.

She heard him groan. Then he had pushed himself away from her and was standing again.

"Jason...?" The word was a reckless plea as she gazed up at him.

"It's all the way. You know that." His voice was very quiet.

She could only nod. Off came the shirt, revealing broad shoulders and a muscled chest. Nobody seeing him like this would take him for an artist, Cindy thought, not for the first time, and reveled in the tough maleness.

The shirt fell to the floor, and then his fingers went to the belt that held his trousers. All the while his eyes were on hers, creating a suspense that made it increasingly hard to breathe.

She was tensing herself for the inevitability of what was to come when the doorbell rang. The sound was shrill, almost obscene in the pulsing stillness. Cindy flinched with shock.

"Jason!..."

He uttered a low curse as he stooped for his shirt and slung it over his shoulders, doing up the three lower buttons. "I'll be back." His tone was curtly matter-of-fact as he made for the door.

Cindy lay quite still for a few seconds longer. With Jason gone she found that she was trembling. Through the open window of the bedroom she could hear voices. The rental agent was at the door. He was talking about a flooded drain at the back of the property, asking Jason to accompany him there.

The voices faded as the two men vanished around the side of the house. For the first time Cindy became aware of vibrations, invisible yet strangely tangible, as if passion and emotion had left their mark on the silent air. It came to her that she was in a stranger's room, on a stranger's bed; that she was quite naked.

Such had been the intensity of her emotions and her need when Jason was in the room, that her unclothed state had not embarrassed her. Now she felt exposed and vulnerable.

She sat up quickly, her hands over her body as if she sheltered it from view. Knowledge flooded her, painful and vivid. Jason's lovemaking stemmed only from the fact that the studio had been too dim for work, a pleasurable pursuit that took the place of their usual routine. "You little tart," he had called her, making it clear that lovemaking had nothing to do with caring.

The discussion with the rental agent would not take long. Jason would conduct it matter-of-factly, as if nothing of moment had been disturbed by the man's arrival. And when the man had gone he would return to the bedroom, confident that the earlier mood had remained constant, and that they would resume making love where they had left off.

But the mood was fragmented. With the severing of a physical contact that had robbed her of all reason, sanity had returned. While Cindy's body ached for fulfillment, her mind dictated that she could not wait here for Jason's return. Much as she longed to be in his arms again, she knew, too, that she would feel even worse later, when she was alone. There would be a sense of cheapness and degradation; the knowledge that what she had done out of love had been for Jason no more than an enjoyable game.

Love! The one emotion she had hoped never to feel for Jason again. Somehow love had been reborn in the short time that he had been here. Or had it never really died? Had it been with her all these years, beneath the hurt and the resentment and most recently the hatred, surfacing at a moment when her defenses had been at a low point?

Feeling for him as she did, she had to leave the cottage before he returned. While a part of her longed for his lovemaking, she knew that the contempt and dislike he had for her as a person would make the act intolerable.

She must move quickly. Any moment now his discussion with the rental agent would end. Getting off the bed, she hurried through the silent passage to the studio. Trembling fingers tugged on shirt and jeans. She was pulling on her sandals when she heard returning voices.

Wildly she looked around her. Had she left her exit too late? Jason would come through the front door of the cottage and her escape would be blocked. And then her eyes alighted on a door that led into the garden—a side entrance that she had never used. In her panic she had forgotten it. She heard the front door open and close in the same moment as she left the studio and slipped behind a bushy wall to the road that led to Poinsettia.

CHAPTER EIGHT

IT RAINED INTERMITTENTLY all that day. Cindy waited a while for the skies to clear before she fetched Jeremy. Eventually she slipped on a raincoat and walked to the Langley farm. The rain had hardened again when she got there, and Mrs. Langley insisted that she stay for tea. When Graham came home he would give them a lift back to Poinsettia.

It rained all weekend and by Monday the sky was still overcast. There would be no sitting for Jason that day, Cindy knew. He had made the position clear enough on Friday; there was no need for her to go to the cottage to consult with him.

Saturday and Sunday had been strange days. Cindy had lived through them in a kind of daze. Graham had spent some time at Poinsettia, and had taken Cindy and Jeremy for a drive. He had recovered all his good humor; if he had noticed

144

Cindy's own preoccupied state he had not commented on it.

Since the flight from the cottage she had not seen Jason. She had half expected that he would pound on her door, demanding to know why she had left so abruptly, but there had been no sign of him. She had been nervous of a confrontation, not quite knowing how she would deal with it. When he did not come she should have been relieved; paradoxically she was disappointed. Jason's behavior showed his lack of interest, she reflected with a touch of despair. He felt absolutely nothing for her.

Tuesday morning dawned, and as the haze lifted from the sea a blue sky emerged. If the weather held there would be a sitting tomorrow, Cindy thought. And could not prevent the leaping of her spirits.

She was feeding the chickens when Graham arrived. "Get Jeremy dressed," he said, "we'll go to the beach."

"Playing hooky?" she teased.

"Certainly." The endearing lopsided smile warmed his face. "After all this rain, today was made for hooky."

"The best excuse for skipping work I ever heard," she grinned back at him.

"I agree." An arm went around her shoulder, pulling her affectionately to him. "Bring a sunsuit for Jeremy. And a nice sexy bikini for yourself."

She laughed appreciatively. "Only if you bring your sexiest swimming trunks."

"Another day."

The icy tones had them spinning around. Jason had come upon them unnoticed. The iciness extended to the eyes that studied them with distaste.

"I beg your pardon!" Cindy said when she had found her voice.

"You'll have to postpone your outing for another day." Still the same cool tones, measured and clipped.

Cindy took a deep breath. She did not want to lose her temper in front of Graham and Jeremy. "I don't think you've met," she said very politely. "Graham, this is Jason Peel. Jason—Graham Langley."

"What has our outing to do with you?" Graham normally friendly, ignored the introduction. His face had assumed a flushed and defensive expression.

"Everything. Cindy will be sitting for me this morning."

"It's Tuesday," she burst out.

"You didn't come to the studio yesterday," he reminded her.

"Because it was raining. Last time...." She broke off, biting her lip. After a moment she said, "You know yourself there was not enough light."

His mouth curved derisively. It was clear that he had not forgotten a moment of their last meeting. "That's why you will come today instead."

146

"Tomorrow." She spoke as firmly as she was able. For some reason it seemed important to make a stand.

"Today."

"Look, Mr. Peel—" anger had made Graham's voice higher than usual "—you can't lay down the law to Cindy like this."

"No?" he said pleasantly.

"Your arrangement with her is Mondays, Wednesdays and Fridays."

"I've already told her why I expect her. We've missed two days."

"Two?" Graham turned to stare at Cindy.

"Yes." Had he noticed that she had hesitated just a moment too long? And then, turning to Jason, she said, "Graham and I had planned an outing. Would one day make such a difference?"

"It would." He offered no explanation. Jason Peel was not given to apologizing or explaining when he felt the issue did not merit it.

"Don't go," Graham urged her. "Mr. Peel can't force you."

Jason shrugged. Seeing the glimmer of amusement in the dark eyes Cindy tensed. Instinctively she knew that he had the upper hand.

"That's quite true." His tone was sleek and soft and dangerous. "You may do exactly as you wish." He paused, very slightly. "But I must warn you that if you refuse to come you may have to consider our arrangement as ended."

A moment of shocked silence followed his words. Then Graham said bitterly, "That's blackmail! Call his bluff, Cindy. Don't go!"

At that moment Jeremy approached with a bucket. Beneath the mud that stained his cheeks he was very pale, and one foot dragged just a little. Cindy looked at him for a long moment, and then back at Jason. "I'll come," she said flatly. "Give me half an hour."

Jason left, leaving a strained silence behind him. Unhappily Cindy looked at Graham. His eyes were stormy, his face flushed.

"Graham...." She put a tentative hand on his arm and saw a muscle tense beneath her touch. "Can we take a rain check on our outing?"

The resentment in the curve of his mouth saddened her. "You know how I feel about this."

"Yes. But you also know.... Jeremy's operation...." She paused a moment. From Jason she expected hardness; from Graham she had hoped for sympathy. "Please, Graham, won't you try to understand?"

"It seems I have no option." He studied her a long moment, a curious expression in eyes that were normally open and guileless. "What did Peel mean when he said you'd missed two days?"

"The rain began on Friday," she said, a little uncertainly.

"You brought Jeremy to my mother."

She glanced at her watch. There were still things

she had to do. Jason would be expecting her. He would show no mercy if she kept him waiting.

"That's right. I didn't know then it would be too dark for a sitting."

"You were gone a long time." She had never seen Graham quite so persistent; had never noticed a certain petulance in his face. "If you weren't sitting for the man, what were you doing?"

He had no right to put her through this. From Jason there were certain things she had to accept, because she had no choice. But not from Graham— nor from anybody else. "Is this an inquisition?" she asked lightly.

"No, sweetheart." Her feelings must have registered for he was instantly remorseful. "I just can't stand the thought of you alone with the man. You...you must have had things to talk about...."

"We did." And before the matter could get out of hand, "It's getting late. I'm going to get Jeremy cleaned up. Could you do me a favor and take him to your mother?"

"DID YOU HAVE TO BE quite so rude to Graham?" Cindy asked bitterly half an hour later.

"Rude?" A lift of one eyebrow. "I was merely making my position clear." Jason was silent for a few moments as his hand moved over the drawing board. When he looked up again it was with such a sardonic expression that she tensed. She knew what was coming. She had been expecting it since their last encounter.

"So, Cindy, apart from everything else you are also a tease." His words were flat, measured.

There was no point in hedging, in pretending that she did not know to what he referred. "Because I didn't want to sleep with you?" She tossed the words at him as lightly as she could.

"You *did* want to. Your responses made that quite clear. You wanted it every bit as much as I did."

She could not deny it. The memory of her behavior was too vivid; had been vivid in her mind all weekend, almost to the exclusion of anything else. "I changed my mind."

"That seems to be a habit of yours." His glance swept her coldly, blatantly, taking in every detail of her appearance from the flushed face and the angry eyes to the breasts that rose and fell beneath the revealing décolleté, and farther to the length of thigh seductively exposed by the slit of the dress. Normally when she posed for him he studied her with the impersonal eye of the artist; now the expression was solely that of blatant maleness.

"You made no effort to follow me," she said after a moment, at a loss for a more adequate comeback.

"Pursuing reluctant women—particularly when the reluctance is calculated—is not my style." He threw her a malicious grin. "Besides, I have no need to. Willing females are always available. Sea View is no exception."

The pain that knifed at her ribs was so sharp that she had no time to stop herself flinching. At the gleam in Jason's eyes—satisfaction, perhaps—she sat straighter. She would not, could not, let him know quite how much he had hurt her.

"Just as a point of interest—" his voice was very smooth "—how did you settle your own frustration?"

Through her distress she shot him her most dazzling smile. "I had no difficulty at all."

A tiny muscle tightened in his jaw, but his eyes lost none of their malice. "The compliant Graham, I suppose."

"You may suppose exactly what you like." Her voice was light and brittle. "Will this be a long sitting, Jason?"

"As long as it takes. I've told you that before," he said, with no change in his tone. Clearly she had not succeeded in hurting him as he had hurt her. "Longer if you don't pose properly." And as she flashed him a startled look he added, "I'm painting a street girl, not an angry child."

"You like to hurt me, don't you?" The words burst out before she could stop them.

He looked at her so thoughtfully for a long moment that she wondered what was coming. When he did speak his words took her by surprise. "That pose is all wrong."

151

"You...you haven't answered my question."

"Pull the dress farther off your shoulder. And your leg—the one closest to me—isn't right, either."

"Answer me, Jason!" Frustration was building inside her, tensing her muscles and forming a knot in her stomach. "Don't you see me as a person at all?"

His eyes met hers, and his lips curved in a lazy smile. "I see you as a model, mercenary to the last degree. Which wouldn't be so bad if you were doing your job properly."

Green fire blazed in eyes that were wide and clear and outraged. "You're a rotten swine!" she flung at him.

"There's also a word for girls like you, my dear," he rejoined pleasantly. "Now cut the histrionics. I want to work. Get your pose right."

She could only stare at him, angrier than she had ever been, as stiff and as tense as a little porcupine ready to strike.

"It seems I'll have to arrange the pose myself." She was so angry that she didn't notice the strangeness in his tone. "And don't tell me later that you didn't ask for it."

He was on his feet and moving toward her before she could anticipate him. A hand went to her leg, tilting it upward, letting the slit of the dress expose more of the honey-tanned thigh. His fingers moved with the fabric, sliding over her, lingering on the sensitive areas of her leg just long enough to provoke a tingling that was like needles flaming through her. The torrent of feeling that rushed through her was so strong that she could not move.

As Cindy saw him reach for her chin she could only sit motionless, mesmerized by a hypnotism she could not resist. He turned her chin, maneuvering it to the position he wanted. As he studied the tilt of her head his fingers were on her throat, tantalizing in their lightness, seductive in their position at the little hollow where the pulse beat so quickly that it was as if it wanted to burst from the slender tendons that confined it.

Just when she thought that she could bear no more he released her. Taking a few paces backward he paused once more to study the effect he had created. And then he was approaching once more, and before she could move to protest he was pushing the fabric even farther from her shoulders. At the best of times the deep-cut décolleté revealed the swell of breasts and the hollow between. Now Jason drew the dress sideways, exposing the nipple of one breast.

"No!" she exclaimed in alarm.

"Not quite right," he said consideringly, ignoring her protest.

He bent, and as he caught the nipple between his teeth she felt it harden and swell. In a moment her body was aflame with longing, a flame that coursed through her leaving her weak. His head was against her chest, the dark hair rough against the smooth skin. Involuntarily her hand went to his hair, her fingers clutching it almost convulsively.

He released the nipple abruptly and stood up. She stared at him through eyes that were blurred and confused, so that she did not take in the satisfaction in his expression, nor the odd bleakness that went with it.

"Jason...." She was leaning toward him instinctively, unconcerned with what he might think.

A hand pushed her back against the silk pillow. "No time for games, sweetheart."

The oddness of his tone, even more than the words themselves, cut through her glazed bewilderment. For the first time she saw the cruel set of his lips, the arrogant lift of the head.

"Games?" she echoed numbly.

He shrugged briefly. "You could have had those on Friday."

"Then why...?" The painful whisper tore from a dry throat. "Why did...did you...?"

"Arouse you?" he finished for her bluntly. "Because it seemed called for."

She could not tear her gaze from the gleam in the narrowed gray eyes. He was like some jungle predator, she thought, a lion or perhaps a cheetah, playing with its captive prey.

"You said I was an angry child...." Dimly she understood.

154

"And I needed the street girl." His teeth flashed their wicked white grin. For a moment she could not speak. Could not think of a single thing to say. A hand went to the décolleté, seeking to pull at the fabric, to hide her body from his eyes.

"No!" The order rang out tersely. "That pose is just right." And then, more lazily, with an outrageousness calculated to inflame, "You look ripe for business, Cindy." He paused. "And more than ready."

"You're a swine!" she hurled at him through her pain.

"You called me that just a few minutes ago." He sounded unexpectedly amused. "Don't disappoint me by becoming a bore."

This time she did not answer. There was nothing to say. She saw his gaze on her face, intent and amused. He would miss no detail of her appearance she thought bitterly—not the angry flush on her cheeks or the trembling of her lips or the rise and fall of her exposed breasts. She could not know that besides all these he saw, too, a wounded vulnerability utterly at variance with the theatrical dress and the forced pose. And as she jerked her eyes toward the window to hide the tears that had gathered beneath the lids, she did not know that he saw these, too.

SHE HAD JUST FINISHED in the kitchen after supper when there was a knock at the door. Cindy's muscles bunched inside her. She had nothing to say to Jason. After this morning's humiliation she felt she did not want to speak to him again—ever.

There was another knock. Her inclination was to ignore it. It was enough that he had a lien over her time three times a week; that she was powerless to resist his every arrogant whim merely because her need for the money he would pay her was so urgent. If he thought he could take up her evening hours, as well—the precious hours when she tried to relax and unwind from the intolerable tensions he inflicted on her—then he thought incorrectly.

"Cindy!" A shout—and a voice she recognized.

"Graham...." She opened the door, her expression contrite. "I'm sorry, I didn't know it was you."

"Who else could it have been?" And then, as she did not immediately answer, he said, "Jason Peel! You thought it was Peel."

She'd slipped again. One look at Graham's face told her he was angry. "It crossed my mind," she said uncertainly. "I'm so glad to see you, Graham. With Jeremy asleep it's so quiet in the house. It's good to have company."

She was talking too much, she realized as they sat down in cane chairs on the little stone patio. Graham's expression had something to do with that; her own embarrassment, too. She had never been ill at ease with Graham before. He was the one friend she had cherished in her years at Sea

View. A new spurt of anger directed itself against Jason.

"You'll have something cool to drink?" she offered.

"No thanks."

"I've some beer in the fridge."

"No." His tone was abrupt. "We have to talk, Cindy."

Her fingers curled in her palms as she took a deep breath and looked out over the orchards. It was a view she had never ceased to enjoy: the rows of trees, the leaves lushly green, the branches heavy with peaches and nectarines and velvet-skinned mangoes; the banana palms, wild and free, a cluster of them at one end of the orchard, the long feathered foliage sharply etched against the sky; the gentle roll and dip of hill and valley toward the sea. The last remnants of sunset hovered in the west, a muted vermilion, gilding the haze that hung over the sea and blurring the horizon. Today the view failed to give her pleasure.

"I'm sorry about this morning," she said, still keeping her gaze on the view.

"It has to end." He sounded angry.

She turned. "It isn't possible."

"You can't go on like this!"

Her voice was very soft. "I have to."

His hand reached for hers, in his fingers an urgency that she had never felt before. "The situation is intolerable. How could Peel be so arbitrary this morning?"

"He did have a point," she said, and wondered why Jason needed defending. "Yesterday there was no sun."

Graham was silent a moment. When he spoke again his tone had altered. "Does the fellow have some sort of hold over you, Cindy?"

Yes! I love him. I loved him three years ago. I love him now. I hate him for what he's doing to me and yet I love him. I always will.

Aloud she said, as calmly as she was able, "We have an agreement. I sit for him. He pays me. It's as simple as that."

"Is the portrait nearly finished?"

As long as it takes, Jason had said. "I don't know."

"Call it a day." It had the tone of an order.

She looked at him with troubled eyes. "I'd have done so long ago if I could."

"Then you don't enjoy what you're doing?" There was an odd note in his voice.

"Enjoy?" She wondered what Graham would say if he could see the transparent flame-colored dress with the hip-high slit and the seductive décolleté; if he knew the image she was meant to portray; if he had any inkling of the lengths to which Jason went in order to produce that image. Unbidden the memory returned of the moment when he had caught her nipple between his lips merely to see it harden. An involuntary shudder passed through her.

"Then you don't enjoy it?"

If only Graham would change the subject. His persistence was beginning to annoy her. And that, too, could be laid at Jason's door, she thought resentfully.

"No," she said quietly. "I don't. But I need the money. Jeremy's operation.... There's no alternative."

"There is—now."

She jerked her head up quickly, caught by his tone. "I don't understand."

"I've been offered a partnership. Dr. Vincent is getting old. He wants me to take over his practice, most of it, anyway." He paused. Then he said, "I want you to marry me, Cindy."

Tears brimmed suddenly in her eyes and in her throat was a lump. She swallowed it back. "Graham...."

"We've discussed this before. But until now I had nothing to offer you." There was a new firmness in his manner. "Now I have."

"Oh, Graham, I'm so glad for you. But—"

"Don't you see," he interrupted her, "you won't need Jason Peel's money. I'll adopt Jeremy. And I'll care for him. I'll care for you both. Well, Cindy?"

It was the solution to everything—the money she needed, her aloneness, her need to have someone other than Jason to think about.

"I love you," he said, when she didn't answer.

The correct response should have been, "I love

you, too." But she couldn't say it. Not now. Perhaps never. She could only look at him, her eyes shimmering with tears.

He stood up suddenly, pulling her with him. And then she was in his arms. His arms were as urgent as his fingers had been, and there was passion in his lips. After a moment Cindy put her arms around his neck. She had to feel *something*, said a desperate voice inside her, it was not possible to feel nothing but the pressure of one mouth against another. Surely Jason could not have destroyed her capacity to feel. But as she tried to respond to Graham's embrace there was nothing but emptiness. An emptiness that communicated itself to him.

He released her abruptly, his hands going to her shoulders as he took a step away from her. "I'd hoped for more."

She could only look at him, pleading wordlessly for his understanding. There was a wounded look in his eyes that hurt her. She could empathize with his feelings. She knew what it was to feel rejected.

"I'm so fond of you," she whispered.

"Fond!" He tossed off the word violently. "I want your love, Cindy." And then with new hope he said, "But that will come." And with even greater conviction, "I know it will."

He made as if to draw her against him again, but she held him off. "Give me time," she said quietly.

"Then you *will* marry me?"

"Graham...."

"Think about it."

"I'll do that," she said after a moment.

He left early. It was as if there was nothing they could talk about after what had happened. Cindy walked a little way down the path with him. As she watched him drive away she felt very sad. Their relationship had been a satisfying one. Whatever her decision, things could never be the same between them again.

With Graham gone the house seemed very quiet, almost claustrophobic. Restlessly Cindy paced the kitchen floor. The ticking of the clock on the wall seemed unnaturally loud, jarring her frayed nerves. Suddenly she felt as if she could not bear to be indoors a moment longer. Going into Jeremy's room she stood for a few seconds by his bed. His breathing was slow and even. He would not miss her if she went outside.

She walked a little way through the garden, stopping at a flat boulder that was just close enough to the house to allow her to hear Jeremy if he should wake up and cry.

Dusk had given way to darkness. Cindy could no longer see the orchards or the sea. There was no moon and the coastal sky was clouded, blotting out the stars. But the perfumes were there—the saltiness of the sea, the mingled scents of ripe fruit, the headiness of the tropical shrubs. And the sounds were there—the thunder of the waves and the hissing of the night insects. Occasional lightning streaked the sky, casting a sheen over the sea. And a little way to the right, where the path that was now invisible made a bend, a single light burned in a dark cottage.

What was Jason doing? Was he reading or listening to music, perhaps? Was he writing a letter to Beulah Mason or to one of the other women in Durban who awaited his return? Or was he in the studio looking at the unfinished portrait, planning what he would accomplish at the next session? Remembering the one that had just passed?

What would Jason's reaction be to Graham's proposal, she wondered. Probably no more than an indifferent shrug from one who did not care what she decided one way or another. Or perhaps a sardonic smile coupled with a malicious remark that the unsuspecting Graham had no idea what he was letting himself in for. But whatever his reaction, it would not be one of disappointment.

Could she marry Graham? It was a question she must face. And soon.

By all standards of logic the answer could be only yes. Graham was a fine man. He was kind and gentle; in marriage he would be steadfast and loyal. He would give her a sense of direction, would be at her side through the heartbreaking months that lay ahead. Not only would he be a father to Jeremy, he would provide the companionship and stability she herself so badly needed.

For all of which he would get what in return? A wife who would cook for him, who would keep his house clean, who would share his bed at night and pretend to an ardor she did not feel.

Love would come with time, Graham had said. In normal circumstances Cindy might well have agreed with him. All the ingredients were there—a deep affection, shared interests, the will to strive together toward a happy home. But these were not normal circumstances. For Cindy was in love with another man. Deeply and wholeheartedly in love. Irrevocably and forever, so it seemed.

If ever there had been a time when love might have been destroyed, that time would have been today. Jason had humiliated her beyond endurance, had made his contempt clearer than ever. And yet through it all she still loved him. Though she would deny the fact to him with her last breath, to herself she had to acknowledge that if Jason were to appear now and take her in his arms, she would be powerless to resist him.

Graham's kisses had been enjoyable. They had given warmth and comfort and the reassurance that she was desirable in at least one man's eyes. But they had failed to stir her. Jason's kisses were something quite different. They set the blood pounding in her veins, and a fire racing through her loins. They made her feel sensuously female even when she knew that the motive for his lovemaking was no more than punishment. They made her feel alive and vital and longing for his touch even when she knew that there could be no future in it; knew, too, that each contact with him could lead only to more unhappiness in the long run.

Marriage to Graham was the sensible course. But it would not be the right thing for Graham. Neither, she understood finally, would it be right for herself.

CHAPTER NINE

CINDY WAS CLOSING THE KITCHEN DOOR when the telephone rang. "Cindy?" Mrs. Langley's voice came through the line, muffled and a little concerned. "I'm so glad I caught you in time. Cindy, love, I seem to have a touch of flu."

Cindy glanced through the open door at Jeremy, who was kicking a ball on the grass. The last thing he needed at this time was contact with a sick person. "I hope you're not feeling too bad?" she asked, her voice warm with concern.

"A day or two in bed, the doctor says; then I'll be fine. But there's Jeremy.... I'm really sorry, love. I know you were counting on me."

"Take care of yourself and get well. And don't worry about Jeremy. I'll manage." Cindy spoke with a reassuring conviction. But as she knocked on Jason's door she wondered how he would take the news. Would he be understanding, or would he insist that work continue as usual? If he did there would be a clash of wills. She had given in to him on almost everything until now, but under no circumstances would she agree to pose in the seductive dress in the presence of her child.

He stood in the doorway, tall and sinuous and compellingly virile, and looked down at the child who was his son. His eyes were narrowed and thoughtful. Then, as if he had not heard a word of Cindy's explanation, he commanded, "Come in the studio."

"No!" Green eyes flashed indignant protest. "Even you can't expect me to pose as a . . . in front of a two-year-old."

His eyebrows rose just a fraction. "Dramatic as usual. I want to do some facial details." And as she relaxed enough to look at him warily, "I'm not quite the demon you think of me. Now come along."

Jeremy was fascinated with the studio and everything in it. Cindy was nervous that he would touch Jason's things, thereby incurring his wrath, but for once Jason showed unexpected patience. He settled Jeremy at a little table in line with his own drawing board, and gave him paper and pencils. "I'm drawing your mommy," he told him. "See if you can draw her, too."

For a while there was silence. Delighted with the novelty of the situation, Jeremy scrawled with absorbed concentration. Jason busied himself with his own work. His eyes went continually to Cindy's face, searching, studying, assessing. The eyes of an artist, she knew, seeking only to establish the line and shade and form he needed, and yet beneath the intentness of his gaze she found it difficult to keep her expression even. For some reason it was even more difficult to keep her pose while Jason drew her face than it was when he had worked on her body.

"Tired," Jeremy announced suddenly, throwing down his pencil.

Jason turned his head to look at him. Now it would come, Cindy thought apprehensively; the explosion she had feared all along. Jason's new patient guise was one she mistrusted.

"You are?" There was no touch of anger in the question, just man-to-man interest.

"Wanna play."

"Do you know," Jason said, before Cindy could speak, "I feel like playing, too. How about a drive and then the beach?"

"I really don't think—" Cindy began.

But she was interrupted by Jason's, "We could even get some ice cream."

"Oh, no, thanks, but—"

The protest died on Cindy's lips as the little boy cried, "Icey! Want icey!"

"And that seems to settle that." For the first time Jason turned to Cindy, and she saw the mischief in the curve of his lips. "Let's get going, shall we?"

"Oh, but...." She bit her lip. "I understand if you don't feel like working today. But the beach.... Well, you really can't want us to go with you."

"I wonder, my dear Cindy, whether you have any idea at all of my wants."

She glanced up quickly, caught by the odd note in his tone. The expression in his eyes was familiarly mocking. But with it there was something else. Something that set her heartbeat racing. And then, as it came to her that she was seeing things that did not exist, that could not exist in Jason, the racing beats slowed.

She did not answer the question—if indeed it had been that. Instead she looked at her son. His face was rosy with excitement. A day on the beach would be a treat. He had had few enough of those lately and would have even less in the months to come. If she denied him his fun it would be only for reasons that did not concern him.

"All right." For the first time in three years she smiled directly at Jason. She thought she heard him catch his breath, and there was a tiny movement in the long column of his throat. Again she was caught by a feeling of wonderment and excitement, so that her lungs felt suddenly tight. And again she knew she had been imagining things when he merely said, "Let's get going, then."

The next hours were strange ones. For Cindy

there was a sense of déjà vu, of repeating obser-
vations and experiences that had once been part of
a six-week time of enchantment. For the first time
since meeting Jason again, she saw him relaxed. It
was as if Jeremy—his son if only he knew it—was
the catalyst that was needed to reveal the man she
had fallen in love with so long ago. There were nuances she had forgotten, little mannerisms; once,
when Jeremy said something funny, there was a
burst of laughter, the sound low and husky and
genuinely amused. It brought a lump to Cindy's
throat.

Sitting beside him in his car, watching the long-
fingered hands on the wheel, well shaped and com-
petent, it was as if the years fell away so that this
drive and the ones to beaches long ago seemed to
merge into a single experience. The lump in her
throat grew.

The car left the highway and slid onto a side
road that had been cut through a belt of unculti-
vated land. On each side was jungle, a luxuriant
mass of tropical undergrowth where trees and
shrubs twisted and twined as they reached for the
sun; an undergrowth so thick that only a well-
booted man would venture through it.

Emerging from the jungle they came to the
beach. Leaving the car in the shade of a giant flame
tree, they took off their shoes and walked onto the
sand. Jeremy had his ball and he ran on the sand,
smoothly damp where the tide had recently left it.

At the edge of the water he stopped, giving little cries of glee when the last foam of the incoming waves curled around his toes. In a rare moment of communication the two adults shared a smile. As Jason turned toward the sea once more, Cindy felt a strange sensation somewhere in the region of her chest.

Jason bought ice cream from a passing vendor, and for a while Jeremy sat silently on the sand, tongue licking at the melting treat. When he had finished, he and Jason began a game with the ball.

Cindy did not join them. She sat on the sand watching the two males whom she loved more than life itself: the little boy who was the focus of her days and whose health was a constant worry, and the tall man who had played his part in giving him birth. A stranger might have taken them for a family, she thought; might even have noticed a little of the similarity between the child and his father despite the fact that he had his mother's coloring.

Now and then Jason glanced her way, as if inviting her to join the game. But she remained sitting. There was a sense of rightness in the unexpected rapport between the man and the child—father and son enjoying a game of ball on a tide-swept beach. It was a scene she knew she would remember long after Jason had vanished from their lives.

Jeremy chuckled and gurgled and shouted with glee as the ball bumped over the sand. Then suddenly he grew tired. He loped over to Cindy, put his head on her lap and his thumb in his mouth. As he fell asleep she moved him slightly, pillowing his head in a more comfortable position. Looking around for something to shield his head from the sun, she saw the little cardigan he had discarded. Very gently, so as not to waken him, she laid it over him.

She did not know what made her look up. Jason was watching her, an expression in his face that was as intent as it was disturbing.

"Jeremy seems very tired," Jason observed.

"After all that romping...." It was hard to speak casually.

"Not all that much of it. He seems to tire very easily."

Jason had always been perceptive. That he should be so now should come as no surprise. "No more so than other children," Cindy managed.

"I don't think that's quite true." A hand reached for her chin, cupping it gently, tilting her face toward his until she had to look at him. "Cindy, is there something wrong with Jeremy?"

Now was the moment to tell him the truth. She had tried so hard to be strong, to bear the urgency of the situation on her own. But the aloneness was weighing on her. And who more fitting to share the problem with than Jeremy's father?

The hand was still beneath her chin, the fingers firm and yet with a kind of tenderness she had forgotten. A thumb moved very slowly down her throat, and though the movement was still gentle it was also almost unbearably sensual.

Tell Jason! Every fiber of her being urged her to take the problem and put it in his hands, not to surrender it but to share it. Jason was strong, not only in physical terms but in a spiritual way, also. Graham was an understanding friend: Jason would be the spiritual crutch she so badly needed.

Somehow she forced her eyes to meet his as she battled the temptation. "There's nothing wrong with Jeremy."

"I'm glad," Jason said lightly, and Cindy thought the matter was ended. After a slight pause he added, with a new inflection in his tone, "If there was something—I hope you would tell me about it."

The lump in her throat rendered speech impossible, and the tears that gathered behind her eyelids made it necessary to pull away from him. As she lowered her head, pretending to brush invisible specks of sand from Jeremy's back, it was hard to keep the tears from falling.

"Cindy." It was a voice she remembered from three years before, quiet and serious. "Why do you sit for me?"

The temptation to tell him the truth was stronger than ever. But somewhere deep inside her was the knowledge that she could not give in. "For money," she said flatly, still without looking at him.

"Money for clothes?"

"Yes."

A small pause. And then he asked, very quietly, "You're sure it's not money you need for something else?"

"Something else?" The words jerked in her throat. "What else could there possibly be, for heaven's sake?"

"Jeremy." Just one word, softly spoken, and all the more dangerous for it.

"You're imagining things!" Cindy jerked up her head, unaware that he would see the tears that brimmed on her lashes and the despair etched in her face. "I want new clothes. Things for the house. Can't you accept that?"

"While I have to," Jason murmured enigmatically. And then, "The sun is very hot on Jeremy's head. I'll lift him off your lap and we'll find some shade."

MRS. LANGLEY recovered quickly from her illness, and two days later she was able to look after Jeremy again. Cindy was relieved. The day spent with Jeremy and Jason had had a poignancy she was in no hurry to repeat. There had been moments when she had come too dangerously near to revealing facts that she had vowed to keep secret. And later, when Jason had dropped them both at Poinsettia, she had been filled with an unsettled feeling that had remained with her for the rest of the day and

173

throughout the night. With Jeremy cared for by Graham's mother, there would be a return to what was by now a well-established routine.

How much longer would the sittings last, she wondered as she tidied the kitchen preparatory to taking Jeremy to Mrs. Langley. So far Jason had not shown her the portrait, and much as she had once wanted to see it, the desire had vanished. Now she only wanted the sittings to come to an end. Jeremy's increasing frailty was on her mind all the time. She needed Jason's payment, and she needed it soon.

With the end of the sittings Jason would return to Durban. He had gathered material for several landscapes, Cindy knew. All that still kept him in Sea View, she thought, was the portrait. With his departure a part of her would die. And yet it was time that he left. For the longer he stayed the less possibility existed that she would ever reach the point where she could accept a life without him.

Had she not been so absorbed in her thoughts Cindy might have noticed Jeremy vanishing through the farmhouse door and toddling down the path that led to the road. A butterfly hovered just inches above him, its wings bright hued. His hands reached for it but never grasped it. Always the butterfly flew just a little beyond him, the erratic movement tantalizing and hypnotic.

Out of the grounds of Poinsettia flew the insect, the little boy hurrying after it. How he would catch the butterfly he had no idea. His two-year-old mind knew only that he had to have it. Along a strange road he ran, one he had never traveled with his mother, and so entranced was he with his mission that by the time his mother began to call his name he did not hear her.

"Jeremy! Jeremy!" There was no panic at first as Cindy looked for her son. He was not in the house, for she had glanced through all the rooms. And he was not on the patch of lawn where he usually played. He must be somewhere in the grounds, absorbed in a game. She glanced at her watch. She was due at Jason's within the hour, and it would not do to be late.

But Jeremy was not in the grounds of Poinsettia. As the realization set in, beads of sweat stood on Cindy's forehead. "Jeremy!" Now her voice was all at once high with fear. He had to be somewhere!

A dusty path led to the gate. In the soft sand was a row of tiny footprints. At the sight she felt a surge of relief. She would follow his tracks.

But outside Poinsettia the footprints ended. The road was rutted, the earth hard-packed, and there was no sign at all of which way he had gone. A maze of country roads ran in all directions, roads that serviced the many small farms of the district. Jeremy could have taken any one of them.

Help—she must have help. Anything could happen to a two-year-old child wandering around alone with no road sense and no experience of looking after himself. Graham.... She would phone Graham, and if he was at home he would come and help her search.

She was about to run back to the farmhouse to phone Graham when another name came to mind. Jason! The father of her child. The one man on whom to lean in time of trouble. The man to whom she would entrust her child and her life.

As she ran the distance to his cottage it came to her that Jeremy could be there. He still babbled in his baby way about the "icey" and the beach. Jeremy could be with Jason. Hope leaped inside her.

The cottage had an air of desolation as the gate swung open on the rusty hinges. If Jeremy was here there was no apparent sign of him.

Cindy knocked on the door, and then, without waiting for a response, she knocked again, sharp raps of impatience. Still no response. She ran down the steps and around the cottage. Jason at least must be here.

But the windows of the cottage were closed. And when she came to the garage it was empty. She stopped short, her hand going to an aching temple as she stared at the place where the car should stand. Jason was out. It was early still; he was not expecting her for another half hour. He must have gone to the village for supplies.

She could run back to Poinsettia and phone Graham. But the chances were that Graham was by now out on his rounds. And in the meanwhile precious time would be lost. She must continue the search on her own.

She was about to leave the cottage when some impulse stopped her. Groping in the pocket of her jeans, she found a pencil stub and a scrap of paper. She wrote a hurried message to Jason, telling him Jeremy was lost; she would be a little late for the sitting. She pushed the message through a slit in the door.

Back through the creaky gate, and a quick look both ways. Still no sign of Jeremy. Running a frenzied hand through a tangle of curls, Cindy wondered where to search first. The beach.... Jeremy loved the beach, even more so since the day on the sands with Jason. That was where he might be headed.

Her heart beat painfully against her rib cage as she took the path that led seaward. It was a long walk to the beach, longer than she would normally expect Jeremy to manage. But there were times when the little boy was unexpectedly tenacious. And she had no idea how long he had been gone. She began to run. If Jeremy was in fact on the sands where the tide was even now coming in, he would be in great danger.

She called his name as she ran. "Jeremy! Jeremy!" Over and over again, hoping against hope that he would hear her and answer her. But apart from the wind-torn cry the only sounds came from the screaming gulls and the roar of the sea.

She was on the beach at last. The day was over-cast and windy, and the sands were deserted. There was nobody whom she could ask for help, nobody who could tell her if a small lost boy had passed this way. The tide was almost in, and the waves were great walls of crashing foam. Normally it was a sight that appealed to some wild streak deep in-side her; today it filled her with dread.

The beach was broken by a pile of rocks. When the tide was out it was possible to walk for miles; now the thrust of the waves made that impossible. There was only one way to get beyond the rocks, and that was by climbing.

For a moment she hesitated, wondering if she should go back the way she had come and look elsewhere. Jeremy would have been unable to ne-gotiate the tide-lashed rocks. But there were other paths leading to the beach, and he might well have taken one of them. He could be on the sands on the other side of the rocks. She had to make sure he was not there.

A little desperately she gauged the way she would have to take. When the tide was out these rocks were dry, but now pools of seawater eddied around them. The going would be hazardous.

There was no option. She could go back the way she had come, taking the path that led through a tangle of palm trees and thorny brush, and then find a path that led to the next stretch of beach. That way would be easier; it would also be more time-consuming. And time was the one thing she did not have.

Taking off her sandals Cindy threw them on the sand. Then she began the climb. The going was even harder than she had anticipated. The tops of the rocks were sharp and pointed, bearing into the soft centers of her soles with a pain that took her breath. Even more treacherous than the jagged surfaces were the stretches of sea moss, slippery stretches where an unfamiliar foot could find no hold. Twice she lost her footing. Once she managed to save herself by lurching out and grabbing a jagged edge. The second time she fell, submerged for a few moments in a murky tidewater pool, then pulled herself up again.

Now and then she stopped and looked ahead to the edge beyond the rocks. Not much farther to go, she consoled herself. If Jeremy was not on the beach she would take the cliff path back, and go on searching elsewhere.

She was negotiating the downward slope of the rock pile when the wave hit her. Until now she had been careful, watching each wave as it came, standing braced and still until it passed, her hands gripping whatever they could find to hold her steady. This wave she did not see, perhaps because impatience had made her careless.

It caught her from behind, knocking her feet from under her. Blindly she lurched out with her hands—a mussel-covered hold was just within

179

reach. But the water dragged her forward. As her hands missed the hold, her head struck the side of a rock. She lay still as the last of the wave swirled over her.

CONSCIOUSNESS RETURNED SLOWLY. There was a sense of drowsy wakefulness, a flash of light behind closed eyes. There were heavy lids, too heavy to open. There was a dry throat and a great thirst and a heat that engulfed her body. There was an aching head and a sensation of something alien affixed to it.

And then there were the images. Voices that came and went, one in particular that was strange and yet totally familiar. There was the sense of a presence, near to her and yet too ethereal to have any substance. There was the touch of hands, coaxing liquid through her lips, smoothing the bed-clothes, caressing her forehead and stroking her hair.

And through it all was a sensation of anxiety, an anxiety that had no form and no nature. Concentrate. She must concentrate.... And in the effort the consciousness slipped away again.

The next wakeful period lasted a little longer. This time when Cindy made an effort to open her eyes her lids fluttered just a little.

"Cindy...." A voice beside her bed. The same voice she had heard before. Both strange and familiar again, with that inexplicable sound in the way it said her name. A voice, Cindy knew, she had heard in dreams. A voice that made her think of Jason. Except that it could not be him.

"Cindy...." A hand touched her cheek, and she felt long fingers linger on her skin. "Darling, can you hear me?"

The endearment shocked her into opening her eyes fully. Jason was sitting beside her bed. He was looking at her intently, with an expression that caused a quickening of her heartbeat.

"I...I've been sleeping?" she questioned uncertainly.

"A long time." His eyes were grave, and there were new lines in his face.

"A long time..." she repeated, puzzled. And then, as it came to her, she sat up with a suddenness that left her dizzy. "Jeremy! I have to find Jeremy!"

"Jeremy's fine." He pushed her gently back against the pillow. "Don't rush things, darling. You'll only make yourself ill again."

Darling! He had said it again. But now was not the time to question why. There were more important things she had to know.

"I've been ill?"

"Very ill. You've had us very worried." A flash of something like pain flitted before his eyes. "But you're better now. Soon you'll be my old Cindy again."

So she had not imagined the sensations she

thought she had dreamed. The hands that had fed her and smoothed her pillow. The anxiety that had hovered in her mind during periods of near consciousness.

"What happened?" she asked at last, very quietly.

He did not answer her directly. "Do you remember anything?"

"Jeremy...Jeremy was lost." Her forehead wrinkled with the effort to remember. "I...I tried to find him. The beach! He was on the beach and I climbed the rocks and...." She stopped. Memory ended with a sliding on a mossy rock face.

"You fell and hit your head," he finished for her. "You were slightly concussed when I found you. And you were lying in a pool of water. Heaven only knows how long you'd been there."

"That's how I got sick?"

"That's right." He nodded, and once more a somber look filled his face. "Thank God your head was above water."

"You saved me, then." She looked at him wonderingly. "And Jeremy, too."

"No, darling, a farmer found Jeremy. He'd wandered into a strange field. It seems he was chasing a butterfly."

"I want to see him." She turned her head inquiringly. The house seemed all at once very quiet. Was Jeremy sleeping?

"You will. I'll bring him to you this afternoon."

Bring...? So he wasn't in the farmhouse after all. Stupid of her not to have realized it. Jeremy could not have remained at home while she was in no position to look after him.

"He's been sleeping at Mrs. Langley's then?"

Jason was quiet for a long moment. His gaze lingered on the small white face on the pillow, noting eyes that were wide and green and puzzled, and lips that trembled quite suddenly and for no apparent reason. "Mrs. Langley has been caring for him during the day," he acknowledged quietly. "But Jeremy has been sleeping at my cottage at night."

"Your cottage?" It was becoming hard to breathe. "But Jason...why?"

A hand reached for one of hers, the fingers closing over it gently but firmly. "You know why."

For long moments they looked at each other, gray eyes holding green ones. There was a lump in Cindy's throat, and until she swallowed it away no words would come. In any event she did not know what to say.

At length, when the silence became almost tangible, she whispered, "Then you know...that...."

"That Jeremy is my son," he finished for her. "Yes, my darling Cindy, I do know." He paused. After a moment he went on, "I know, too, that he is a very sick little boy, and that the reason you sat for me...that you endured all I put you through—" his lips tightened "—was that you needed the money for an operation."

Blindly she shook her head. "You weren't supposed to know."

"But I do. Cindy, Jeremy will be all right. I've seen the specialist. The operation will take place next month and our son will be all right."

Our son.... "How did you know?" she whispered at last.

"I never quite believed the story you concocted. It didn't seem to fit in with the Cindy I thought I knew."

"You went along with it."

"Because that was the game you wanted to play. Darling, when you were so ill I phoned John."

"John?"

"I felt your brother had a right to know. Sally's been here with you much of the time. She's in the kitchen now. Cindy, John and I had a long talk—about you, about Jeremy. John told me something I'd suspected for some time."

"What was that?" The words emerged painfully from a parched throat.

"That you had not been seeing another man before you met me. That there was no Andrew in your life. Never had been." He paused. "That being the case, Jeremy had to be my son."

She closed her eyes. It was all out. She had tried so hard to keep the truth from him, and now her illness had brought it out. He had been calling her "darling" since her return to consciousness. The endearment had thrilled her. Now she guessed at

184

its reason. Despair gripped her as she knew that nothing had changed.

"What are you thinking?"

At the words she opened her eyes. "I was just wondering why you'd been calling me 'darling,'" she said a little dully.

A gleam appeared in the gray eyes as he reached for her chin, cupping it as he had done on the beach, letting a finger trail along the sensitive column of her throat where, despite her resolve to remain passive, it stirred a response she could not suppress. "It's an appropriate endearment for my future wife."

"No!" The word burst out with a vehemence that seemed to astonish him.

"You prefer something else?" he asked.

"No." Somehow she managed to drag her eyes from his, concealing the tears that threatened behind her lids. He was talking of marriage a second time. It was what she yearned for more than anything else. But the circumstances had not changed. She had known three years ago that their marriage could not succeed, and she knew it still.

"I can't marry you...."

"Why not?" He was watching her intently. "Cindy, darling, I imagined that you care for me." The hand on her chin brought her around to face him. "Could I have been wrong?"

The treacherous tears spilled onto her lashes, and the pain-filled eyes held an expression that was easy to read. "I do love you," she admitted. "B-but that's not the point. I can't marry you."

A tear left her lashes and slipped down her cheek. Jason brushed it away. "Tell me why?" His tone was gentle. And when she did not answer, "I have a feeling that whatever the reason, it relates to your running away from me three years ago."

His tenderness was unnerving. She could not marry him, that much she knew. But she owed him an explanation.

"It is the same reason," she began slowly. She looked at him for a moment, then looked away, and this time he did not force her to turn back. "Three years ago when you asked me to marry you it was a question of honor...." She stopped.

"Honor!" he exclaimed.

"I'd slept with you. And...and then...you found out I was a virgin. And...you felt you had to marry me." She turned to look at him. "Don't you see, Jason, it's the same thing again. You know that Jeremy is your son, and so you feel duty bound to marry his mother."

Something came and went in the gray eyes, but otherwise his expression did not change. "Perhaps you'd better explain how you arrived at your deductions."

So he wasn't bothering to deny it. "It wasn't difficult. A woman came to see me. Three days before the wedding. She told me that you were marrying me because you had to."

186

"Her name?" he asked harshly.

"Beulah Mason," Cindy said, and saw the look of understanding in Jason's face. "She told me she'd been having an affair with you. That it would go on even after we were married."

"And so you decided to run away." There was no inflection in his tone.

"Yes." For no reason at all she was suddenly uncertain.

"And you think that because I know Jeremy is my son my sense of honor has surfaced once more."

"Hasn't it?" she challenged him.

"How little you know me." The mocking expression she hated was back in his eyes. "You could have talked to me, Cindy."

"I...I could have," she acknowledged uncertainly. "But there'd have been no point. Wh-what could you have told me?"

"Two things. One, that Beulah was a woman scorned." There was a hard expression in his eyes as he looked at her. "She and I did have an affair of sorts. I'm a man, Cindy. But I ended the affair when I met you. I thought Beulah accepted it. I must have been mistaken."

"You said there were two things," Cindy said softly, her eyes never leaving his face. Her heart was beating very rapidly against her rib cage, and the longing to feel him close to her was well-nigh unbearable.

187

He smiled, a rare smile that warmed his eyes and lighted his face. "I'd have told you that I loved you. I thought you knew it, anyway."

How stupid she had been. How childishly and irrevocably stupid. And now that she had shown her initial mistrust of him, any love he might once have felt for her would have vanished.

"I still love you," he said, as if he guessed her thoughts.

"But the way you treated me.... The things you said...."

"A kind of shock treatment," he admitted ruefully. "And perhaps a childish way of healing a hurt of my own. Cindy, darling, you will marry me?"

Even now, against all reason, she was not convinced. There was Jeremy. Jason's son. Even now he could be tricking her into marriage.

"The portrait," she said uncertainly. "What will happen to that?"

"It will hang above our bed," he told her.

"No!"

"Yes, my darling." He stood up. "I want to show it to you."

She made a gesture of protest. "I don't want to see it."

In one breath he said that he loved her, in another that he wanted to show her the picture he had painted of her as a street girl. There was no future for them after all.

"I want to show it to you," he repeated firmly. "I have it here."

She'd have to see it, she reasoned forlornly. It seemed there was no way of getting out of it. But afterward she would tell him what she had decided: that she could not marry him; that it was best if he forgot that Jeremy was his child, that she would go on living as she had until now.

She watched him leave the room—tall, dark, lithe and so compellingly masculine that she wondered whether she would ever again meet a man who could match up to him. She did not think it was possible.

He came back carrying a canvas. As he came to her bed she felt herself tense. This was a moment she had sometimes imagined, and always with a certain sense of dread. Now that it had come she was strangely frightened.

He stood the canvas against a chair, his body blocking it from view. As he moved away she knew that he was watching her.

For moments that held no meaning in time she could not speak, could not move. Later she was to wonder whether she had breathed. As her eyes were riveted on the picture, she knew that nothing Jason had said or done had prepared her for what she now saw.

The portrait filled most of the canvas. The face was Cindy's, but it was neither the face nor the posture she had expected. There was not a trace of the street girl she had posed as. Nor did she see the flame-colored dress she had grown to hate.

The girl in the picture wore a pink halter-necked dress, the dress Cindy had worn when she had come to tell Jason that she would sit for him. And the face in the portrait was that of a young woman whom pain and love had touched.

It was like looking at her own mirror image, Cindy thought wonderingly, and yet different, too. For when she looked at herself in the mirror she had never glimpsed the very soul that the artist had laid bare. There was innocence in the small gamin face with the eyes that were almost too big. But with the innocence there was maturity, also. There was sadness and there was a certain awakening joy. There were other qualities, too, she saw, and knew that it would take time to fully understand what Jason had depicted. What took no time at all was the understanding that he had painted her as Cindy Greerson, a person whom he seemed to know better almost than she knew herself.

As she turned to him, more moved than she had been in a long while, she did not know that her emotions were in her face, easily readable to the artist who had explored the very fiber of her being.

"I don't understand . . . ." she whispered.

Sitting down on the bed, he took her hand and began to caress her wrist with a slow rhythmic movement that sent an electric tingling up her arm. "I had to come," he said. "When you ran out on me three years ago I was angry. So angry that I did not follow you. But I never stopped loving you."

"Oh, Jason..." she began, hope leaping anew.

"Let me finish." He was smiling, that rare smile that made her want to touch his cheeks, his eyes, and then trace a finger around the curve of his lips. "I tried to tell myself that you were nothing but an immature child. I tried to forget you. At first it wasn't difficult. There were many who were willing to console me. Beulah...." He was quiet a moment, as if he were thinking of the woman who had been responsible for three wasted years.

"Later?" Cindy prompted.

"I couldn't get you out of my mind. I knew that there was more to it all than appeared on the surface. No matter how young you were you didn't seem the kind of girl who'd behave quite so callously. Nor were your responses in character unless you cared about me." He grinned. "Because you were very responsive, my darling." As a warm flush spread over her cheeks his grin widened. "I look forward to more of that when you are better."

"Go on," she pleaded, as eager to hear the rest as she was to draw attention away from herself.

"I decided to seek you out. John was reluctant to give me your address. In the end I wormed it out of your friend Marlene. I thought if I got you to sit for me I'd have a better chance of finding out the truth about the real Cindy."

"Then the pose... the red dress...."

191

"All a sham," he acknowledged. "I knew almost immediately that you were still the girl I'd fallen in love with. I must admit that Jeremy had me puzzled. I wanted to think he was mine, but you were so adamant about that wretched Andrew."

"Would you have shown me the picture?" she asked.

"It was meant to be a wedding present." Gray eyes lingered on her face, noting the glow in eyes that had been sad for too long. "I love you, my darling. Will the picture hang over our bed?"

"Yes! Oh, yes!" She tried to say more as he gathered her to him, folding her head against the strength of his chest; wanted to talk, to explain. But all she managed before he lifted her face was, "I love you, Jason." As his lips came down on hers she realized that no more explanations were necessary. Jason understood her now, as he would forever.